Dear Reader,

Welcome to the newest edition of *Caregiver's Handbook: A guide to caring for the ill, elderly, or disabled—and yourself.* One day you may find that someone you care about—a spouse, parent, relative, or close friend—needs help negotiating the daily tasks of life. Perhaps that day has already come. More than 43 million Americans act as unpaid caregivers, offering assistance with tasks ranging from housekeeping to dressing, toileting, and coordinating doctor visits. Their efforts are indispensable in the lives of people struggling with illness, disability, or the challenges that often accompany aging. If these volunteer caregivers were being paid, the value of their time and service would reach $470 billion annually.

As the very embodiment of love and commitment to others, caregiving is one of the most worthwhile jobs you may ever undertake. However, it can also cause undeniable strain—the average family caregiver spends about 24 hours per week helping a loved one, and those who live with the care recipient put in more than 40 hours a week. More than two-thirds of family caregivers are women, with an average age in their 40s, and many feel unbearably squeezed between the demands of caregiving, the needs of their families, and the pressures of work.

The information in this report will help you meet the needs of the person you care for, while still attending to your own needs. Moreover, it will help you navigate the changes that are taking place in the world of health care. The first chapter focuses on developing a caregiving plan that addresses your loved one's daily care, safety, and basic needs. The chapters that follow describe financial, legal, and medical information that's vital to caregivers. This edition also features a Special Section devoted to caring for yourself as you cope with the stresses that come with caregiving. Throughout the report, you'll find plenty of resources and tips designed to improve your loved one's life, as well as your own.

Which sections of this report you find most useful will depend upon the condition of the person in your care. Some individuals—for example, those with dementia or physically disabling illnesses—will require more hands-on assistance than others. Take whatever is useful for you, with the understanding that information in this report that doesn't apply to your situation today may be relevant in the future, as the person's condition evolves.

My observation as a geriatrician is that the caregiving role can be very isolating, but also very rewarding. We hope that the information in this report helps you feel supported and connected to a larger world of resources and people who know just what you are going through.

Sincerely,

Suzanne Salamon

Suzanne Salamon, M.D.
Medical Editor

Becoming a caregiver

If you're taking on the role of caregiver for the first time, you probably have many questions. What will this role entail? How much time will it take? What will your responsibilities be? Where can you find help? Who will pay for any outside help? How do you even start? This report will deal with all these questions, plus the crucial issue of how to find both physical and emotional support for yourself throughout this process.

You may even be wondering who qualifies as a caregiver? A caregiver is someone who handles many or all of the needs for a loved one or friend who is no longer able to care for himself or herself because of illness, age, or disability. Caregivers can provide their services in many venues—at home, at the hospital, or in visits to a long-term nursing care facility. Some caregivers even live great distances from the person to whom they are providing care.

The spectrum of tasks caregivers undertake is truly vast. Some responsibilities, such as grocery shopping, housekeeping, doing laundry, and cooking, are familiar to us all. Giving injections, changing bandages, calming an agitated parent with Alzheimer's disease, or helping a disabled partner get from the bed to the bathroom can be far more daunting. But through countless unheralded contributions like these, caregivers enable their loved ones to continue to live as independently as possible.

Caregiving can be wonderfully rewarding, but it can also be a drain physically, emotionally, and financially. You may not have asked for this role. Perhaps you were thrown into it unexpectedly, and now find yourself unsure of what to do and unprepared for the road that lies ahead. This handbook will put you on the right path for developing a plan and coping with everyday tasks. Be aware that those tasks can vary dramatically depending on just how debilitated your loved one is and what kind of living situation he or she is in. It's impossible to anticipate every hurdle you will face.

However, gaining insight into many of them—and finding some creative solutions, as you will in this report—will better enable you to cope with the stresses that come with this role. Hopefully, the resources and insights you discover in the following pages will also help relieve some of the worry or guilt you may feel—and help you take steps to preserve your own health and well-being. After all, the better you care for yourself, the better you can care for your loved one.

Developing a plan

You can never plan for every detail or eventuality, as your loved one's needs will almost certainly change over time. But if you have the basics covered, you will have an important foundation to build on, both today and as things evolve over time. Your initial caregiving plan will largely depend on your answers to these five key questions:

- For whom are you caring—an aging parent, an ill partner or friend, or a disabled child or other family member?
- What precipitated the need for care?
- Is the situation time-limited (for example, for someone who needs care while healing from surgery or an injury), or is it likely to continue indefinitely?
- What care or services will your loved one need?
- Aside from basic needs, what does your loved one

want? For example, elderly parents may want to continue living independently at home rather than move in with you or to a nursing home. How can you help meet these goals?

To develop your plan, you first need to think about your caregiving goals. Seeing the person through a devastating illness and back to health may not be a realistic expectation, but you can definitely make it a goal to treat your loved one with compassion and honor his or her dignity at all times (see "Your caregiving goals," at right). Next, have an open, honest conversation with your care recipient about what both of you expect (see "Talking with your loved one," page 4). Finally, turn to the needs questionnaire on page 11 for help in determining just what issues need to be addressed.

Remember that an initial plan is just that—a first step. Change is one of the few certainties of caregiving, so it is important to re-evaluate your situation often. If the situation is fairly stable, reassess your plan every few months. If things are changing rapidly, you may need to reassess from week to week. As time goes on, you may need more assistance from others, such as additional help from family members or outside services. For example, you may want to hire someone for three to four hours a day to help with activities like dressing, preparing meals, grocery shopping, and taking medications. Or you may need to set certain services in place, such as lawn maintenance and snow removal, bill paying, grocery shopping, or meal delivery. Check in frequently to make sure these services are running smoothly.

If possible, try to stay a step or two ahead of your loved one's changing needs by asking doctors and other experts for their assessment of how the situation might progress in the coming weeks, months, or years.

Don't solely base caregiving decisions on the needs and desires of the care recipient, however. Also consider the consequences of those decisions on yourself and other family members. Spend some time reading "Care for the caregiver" (page 45), a Special Section of tips on dealing with caregiver stress and burnout, to get insight into some of the challenges that may await you.

Your caregiving goals

Every caregiver experiences times when it's easy to be patient and loving, and periods when it seems almost impossible to deal with the tasks at hand. Write down what you consider to be the most important elements of good caregiving, to remind you of your goals and underscore the importance of all you do. When creating your list of essential elements, ask other family members and the care recipient what's important to them. Then refer to this list whenever you need a refresher.

The following points may help guide you in creating your list. As you go through this list, you may want to make some quick notes in "My caregiving goals," below.

Caring acts. What kinds of acts make you feel secure and loved? Consider, too, how the recipient defines caring. Beyond traditional caregiving tasks, your loved one may value your willingness to lis-

▶ My caregiving goals

Think carefully about your goals as a caregiver and jot them down. You can make some short notes in the space below as you read this report. The purpose of this list is to help you focus your caregiving efforts and guide you through a variety of situations.

1. Goal: _____
   Ways to act on this: _____
   _____

2. Goal: _____
   Ways to act on this: _____
   _____

3. Goal: _____
   Ways to act on this: _____
   _____

4. Goal: _____
   Ways to act on this: _____
   _____

5. Goal: _____
   Ways to act on this: _____
   _____

ten, a hug or kiss, or a favorite shared meal. Leave the door open for reciprocation. Many people accept care more willingly if they can return the gesture in some way.

Respect. The desire to be treated with respect doesn't change with age or infirmity. Try to respond to the person, not just to the illness or disability.

Dignity. One challenging aspect of caregiving is offering advice or help while still allowing the person to be as self-sufficient as possible. Offering too much assistance can undercut self-esteem, independence, autonomy, and ultimately dignity. Whenever possible, encourage the person you care for to continue making decisions and engaging in productive tasks, such as grocery shopping, bill paying, and going out with friends (see "Staying social," page 5). Older people who become dependent on a caregiver often say they are treated like children. Remind yourself that the person you are caring for is an accomplished adult and address the person with the respect you would show any other adult.

Honesty. It's tough to impart difficult news, such as an unpleasant medical diagnosis, a request that a parent stop driving, or the need to consider long-term care arrangements. Yet softening the blow by shading the truth may compound the problem and is disrespectful to the person involved. It's better to be open with a painful truth and then acknowledge both parties' feelings about it (see "Talking with your loved one," at right).

Foresight. Successful caregiving requires foresight and thought. This applies not only to financial and estate planning, but also to the everyday tasks that come with the job: meal preparation, receiving visitors, and maintaining personal hygiene. By predicting what obstacles might lie ahead, you'll prevent stress and have sufficient time to carefully weigh your options, instead of scrambling to resolve each fullblown crisis as it happens. Just realize that it may take some trial and error to learn the skills needed to handle challenging situations.

Warmth and compassion. Warmth is in the delivery rather than the act itself. It announces its presence in the way you listen to the hundredth rendition of a story, cuddle up to watch a well-loved movie

© kali9 | Getty Images

Caregiving poses many challenges, including offering help without babying the person or treating him in a way that undercuts his self-esteem. Warmth and compassion go a long way.

together, or simply sit and hold a hand. It's easy to lose your compassion and your connection with the person you're caring for when you're tired and overwhelmed and he or she is acting angry and unappreciative. Try not to forget your humanity when you get caught up in the burdens of the caregiving role. Try to step back, and acknowledge and address difficult feelings before they harm your relationship.

Talking with your loved one

Discussing needs with the person who will be receiving care can be a prickly business. Reassure him or

A CAREGIVER'S PERSPECTIVE

"Develop a game plan for the years ahead. Thankfully, somebody advised me of that early on. Our game plan was that we wanted my father to live with us for as long as possible and then have him go to an Alzheimer's unit that's in a great facility that's close to us."

— *Irwin, 52, whose 85-year-old father has Alzheimer's disease*

her that you're not trying to take control away. You simply want to make sure that you address all of you're your loved one's wants and needs.

Starting the discussion

One way to open a conversation is to ask the person to spell out what he or she believes would help. For instance, say: "I've wondered if you're having any trouble with _____." Or, "I've noticed it is getting harder for you to _____." If offers of help are flatly declined, you might call in a second opinion about the need for assistance. Try talking to the person's doctor or to trusted relatives or friends. Their opinions may carry more weight than your own. Some doctors, particularly geriatricians, may be willing to schedule and attend a family conference to talk about what is needed. Geriatric care managers or social workers can also help facilitate these kinds of discussions and present a range of care options (see "Consulting a geriatric care manager," page 6).

If you want to establish plans in advance for certain types of assistance, such as nursing home care and insurance coverage, you might start a conversation by bringing up the value of thinking ahead. For instance, you might say, "I read about Medicaid planning in the news today. Do you know about this?"

Finances or health problems can be particularly difficult to talk about, and it is hard to ask sensitive questions of a relative, spouse, or partner who already feels pressured from illness. Raising concerns about your own financial future can make it easier for you to ask a parent about his or her finances. The same tactic may work well for discussing end-of-life decisions. You may find that the person wants to acknowledge these issues. It can be a relief to talk frankly about troubling topics and share concerns rather than hiding them.

Staying social

Our relationships make us who we are. Most of us thrive on seeing friends, co-workers, and family. Maintaining strong ties is one key to a healthier, happier life. It fosters a sense of belonging and purpose, boosts confidence and self-esteem, prevents loneliness, and wards off Alzheimer's and other forms of dementia.

Unfortunately, as we get older it is often hard to maintain those relationships because of challenges like impaired hearing and vision, compromised mobility and reliance on others to get around, and chronic illnesses that make social interactions taxing. Family and friends move away; longtime friends and loved ones die. Consequently, older adults can lose touch with the world. This physical and social isolation can lead to depression and anxiety. As a caregiver, encourage your loved one to socialize. Teach him or her how to use a computer and navigate the Internet. Set up Skype and other online communication tools. Plan visits at home and away with friends and family members. Find a local adult day program or senior center with activities and opportunities to socialize.

The following tips can help keep your loved one socially active and engaged:

- Sign up your loved one for tai chi, water aerobics, or another group fitness activity at the local senior center.
- Encourage him or her to volunteer in the community.

- Take day trips together to nearby museums, restaurants, or libraries.
- Enroll him or her in a club that shares a common interest, such as bridge, knitting, or books.
- Take a class together in art, cooking, computers, or a foreign language.
- Schedule regular phone or Skype calls with friends and family members who live far away.

In cases where people live in rural areas, are far from family, or aren't very mobile, staying social may require a move. Your loved one can find ample opportunities for social contact by moving to some form of group living, such as a continuing care retirement community or an assisted living community (see "Long-term care," page 42).

Discuss tough decisions honestly

Certain topics—for instance, the need to stop driving or move to a long-term care facility—are painful for everyone concerned to discuss. Even so, telling white lies or making promises that are impossible to keep can come back to haunt you.

For example, few people want to go to a nursing home. Instead of pledging that this will never happen, promise only that you will try hard to work out other solutions for as long as possible. If you know a nursing home is the best long-term option, don't suggest that such a move is just for a few weeks. When those weeks are over, the reckoning and sense of betrayal will be impossible to avoid. It's better to acknowledge that you made this difficult decision with your loved one's best interests at heart.

Put these sentiments into your own words: "I know it's very hard for you to think about moving to a nursing home. But we can't supply all the care you need anymore. I worry about you constantly, especially when I'm not available. I've tried really hard, but I can't keep everything going. We need to think about finding a place where you'll be safe and well cared-for all the time." If appropriate, mention concerns about your own health and well-being or worries about what might happen if you become ill or unable to offer enough care. A single conversation is rarely sufficient. Give the person you are caring for a chance to absorb the difficult news. Moving toward a solution is likely to take time and several discussions.

A CAREGIVER'S PERSPECTIVE

"It's really important to recognize what your loved one truly wants. I have a couple of friends whose parents are staying at home. Their home lives are not ideal. The level of care they're getting is not the highest you could imagine. And yet these people would much rather be in that situation than be in a nursing home."

— *Beth, 41, whose 79-year-old mother needs significant assistance to remain in her home*

▶ Set up a home evaluation

Geriatric care managers, social workers, nurses, physical and occupational therapists, and some physicians may make home visits to get a better picture of a person's daily life. Information gathered during these visits can be used to improve care, safety, home accessibility, and quality of life. Insurance may cover the cost of these home visits.

People are often willing to assume some level of risk to their safety or well-being in exchange for autonomy and personal choice. If a loved one chooses to live in a situation that seems too risky to you, you might need a doctor to help determine the person's decision-making capacity. If your loved one can fully understand the consequences of his or her decisions, then you must abide by them, whether or not you agree with them.

A move to a long-term care facility may become a necessity, but it isn't always financially attainable with the individual's existing resources. The high cost of nursing home care is a serious issue for many families. Although Medicaid covers a very high percentage of nursing home costs, the person needing care may need to deplete a substantial amount of his or her savings to qualify (see "Medicaid," page 32). An elder care attorney can find ways to protect assets for a spouse who still lives at home, if needed. Rest assured that the quality of care will be the same, even if it is covered by Medicaid.

For information on how to pay for nursing homes, see "When your loved one needs more care," page 40.

Consulting a geriatric care manager

When you're entering new territory, a guide who knows the terrain well can help immensely. Geriatric care managers assist older people and families facing challenging care decisions. Their training may include nursing, social work, counseling, or gerontology.

An experienced geriatric care manager can help you navigate the tangles of family dynamics, round up medical care and other necessary services, and coordinate the transmission of information among

Being your own care manager

No quick courses can give you the knowledge and resources of an experienced geriatric care manager, but the following tips may help you better coordinate care.

Get organized. File the paperwork you accumulate under key topics: medical care, benefits, resources, assisted living, nursing homes, and so on.

Have the person's medical history and medications list handy. Keep these in a binder. Many electronic medical record systems now have a patient portal, which gives the patient access to parts of his or her medical record. If you are the health care proxy for the person you are caring for (see "Advance directives," page 26), you can get the same access to the medical record. Many systems have a smartphone application that will give you access to the person's medications, conditions, and other health-related information on your phone.

Come prepared with questions. Always keep a notebook or smartphone handy and write down questions about your loved one's health as you think of them. Bring this list to each medical visit, to ensure that you cover everything you need to address in the limited time you may have with the provider.

Keep a log of conversations with medical professionals. During each conversation, write down the provider's name, when you spoke with him or her, and what you discussed. If certain tasks need to be done—for example, medical tests or appointments—note which ones you'll handle yourself, and which ones you'll assign to other caregivers. (It's a good idea to also keep a written record of conversations with insurers, financial advisers, and lawyers.)

Coordinate medical care. Ideally, one doctor should be in charge of coordinating care, but it may be up to you to keep every specialist who is involved in the loop. Each doctor should know what tests and therapies other providers have recommended, and what medications (both prescription and over-the-counter) the patient is taking. Give your primary care provider's fax number to each of the person's specialists (eye doctor, rheumatologist, cardiologist, etc.). That way, your loved one's main doctor will receive updates from each provider he or she visits.

Ask until you have answers. Don't be afraid or embarrassed to ask for simpler explanations, a breakdown of the risks

and benefits of a particular treatment, or a second opinion.

Be polite, but insistent. If medical personnel give you elusive answers, keep pressing your case. Ask for the best times to call, but call more frequently if necessary. When no one answers, leave a message. Find out if you can communicate by email or through a patient portal, which may be more convenient for doctors. Be friendly to those who answer the phone so they will be more willing to assist you.

Be informed. Gather basic information through reputable websites, national organizations, and other sources to help you prepare for challenging decisions. Not sure where to start? Check with some of the organizations listed in this report (see "Resources," page 52). For reliable information on health conditions, visit the National Institutes of Health's MedlinePlus website (www.medlineplus.gov).

medical personnel. Some of the tasks these professionals routinely undertake are

- evaluating needs
- connecting people to helpful services, senior housing, and long-term care facilities
- bringing families together to supportively discuss options
- hiring and monitoring home care personnel
- accompanying people to doctors' visits when their family members aren't available
- communicating with specialists, hospital and home care staff, and family members to coordinate care
- alerting families to financial, medical, or legal problems and suggesting ways to handle them
- helping with a move to assisted living, a nursing home, an Alzheimer's care unit, or other facilities.

Working with a geriatric care manager can be costly but extremely helpful, especially if you are scrambling to arrange care from far away (see "Long-distance caregiving," page 8). Geriatric care managers usually charge by the hour, and hourly rates can range from $50 to $200. Medicare and Medicaid won't cover the costs, but sometimes long-term care insurance will pick up the tab. More commonly, the client or family pays. Before you hire a geriatric care manager, get a written agreement outlining the scope of services offered and costs involved. This can also help you decide which tasks, if any, family and friends might undertake to save money.

Contact the Aging Life Care Association for more information or to locate a geriatric care manager (see "Resources," page 52).

Long-distance caregiving

What happens when you don't live near the person you are trying to help? Distance may be an issue if you are unable to move because of family or job responsibilities, and you can't bring the person to you. Caring from a distance is stressful in many ways. From afar, it's hard to anticipate needs, supervise care, and handle any problems that arise.

If you're in the position of providing care to a distant friend or family member, these tips can ease some of the difficulties tacked on by the miles between you.

Book regular trips. Travel on workdays whenever possible so that you can line up services (which may not be reachable on the weekend) and deal most effectively with problems. Call several weeks ahead if you plan to interview local caregivers, visit nursing homes, or see local health care providers. If you're checking up

Keep high-tech tabs on your loved ones

About five to seven million caregivers in the United States provide care from a distance, according to the Family Caregiver Alliance. If you're among them, or if you just live in a separate residence, do you worry that your aging mother might accidentally leave her stove on, or your elderly uncle will forget to take his medications? A variety of technologies—from health trackers to home monitoring services—are now available to help caregivers keep tabs on their loved ones' safety and well-being from afar.

However, many caregivers aren't taking advantage of these technologies, despite their willingness to do so. More than 70% of caregivers surveyed by AARP said they were interested in technologies such as home monitoring services. Yet only about 7% were actually using these tools. The most frequently cited barriers to adopting these technologies were a lack of awareness and perceived high cost.

Most people are familiar with the emergency response system known as Lifeline, thanks to its well-known commercial (with the woman who cries, "I've fallen and I can't get up!"). What may be less familiar are remote monitoring services that give you a window into your loved one's daily life. Some of these services, like Care@Home (www.essence-grp.com/smart-care/care-at-home) and Be Close With Amada (www.beclosewithamada.com), use sensors placed throughout the home to detect problems—for example, if the person falls, skips meals, or doesn't get out of bed in the morning. In addition to alerting you to any changes in your loved one's daily routine, Alarm.com's Wellness system (www.alarm.com) automates home security, temperature, and light settings to ease daily responsibilities on those who are aging in place. TruSense (www.mytrusense.com) offers a combination of monitoring services—including fall detection, motion sensors in the home, voice activation

to turn on lights without getting up, and tracking via GPS (global positioning system) to ensure that every outing is completed safely. The Apple Watch Series 4 also offers fall detection. By analyzing wrist trajectory and impact acceleration, Apple Watch sends the user an alert after a fall, which can be dismissed or used to initiate a call to emergency services. If Apple Watch senses immobility for 60 seconds after the notification, it will automatically call emergency services and send a message along with location to emergency contacts.

Courtesy of Apple

The Apple Watch Series 4 offers fall detection.

Technology is also simplifying and streamlining home medical care. LifeFone (www.lifefone.com) offers medication reminders, as well as a daily check-in call to ensure the person is doing well. MedMinder (www.medminder.com) dispenses medications at predetermined times and alerts the caregiver immediately if doses are missed.

Cellphones can make remote care possible in a variety of ways, such as by storing and transmitting vital signs, providing reminders when a measurement or medication is due, or (in phones with GPS capability) serving as a tracking device if a person wanders away. Caregivers can even keep track of their loved one through shoes with GPS-embedded insoles (www.gpssmartsole.com), which transmit a signal whenever the wearer leaves a designated area.

If you think one of these technologies could be helpful for your loved one, ask your geriatric care manager or doctor to recommend an appropriate system.

on local caregivers, it may be better not to give advance notice. When you arrive, look around with the needs questionnaire (see page 11) in mind. How is your relative or friend doing? Is the house clean? Are pantry and fridge reasonably well stocked? Are bills being paid? Also, take time to organize important papers. If possible, make copies of these documents to take home, or at least note where this information is kept.

Set up a safety net. Give your loved one's neighbors or friends a set of house keys. Look into medical alert systems, such as a pendant the person can press if he or she falls or needs help in an emergency. Or, purchase a home monitoring system (see "Keeping high-tech tabs on your loved one," page 8). Have a regular phone-in time to check that everything is fine. Arrange for daily or weekly visits from family or friends, or from assistants you find through a local Agency on Aging (see "What is the Agency on Aging?" at right). Ask a network of friends, relatives, and neighbors to alert you if they notice anything worrisome with your loved one's situation.

Keep a logbook. Note conversations with hands-on caregivers, insurers, medical personnel, and others involved in care. Write down the names of the people you speak to, when you spoke to them, and what suggestions they made. List things that need to be done, and who will handle these tasks.

Keep helpful numbers handy. Put together a single list of doctors, social workers, neighbors, and friends. Also include important state or local agency numbers, such as the local Agency on Aging. The Eldercare Locator (800-677-1116) can link you to the appropriate agency and has information on available community services. Keep copies of these numbers in several places—your smartphone address book, computer, filing cabinets at work and home, and logbook.

Arrange necessary services. Whenever pos-

sible, interview and hire people in person. If that isn't convenient or you need help right away, turn to a local service, such as a home nursing agency, contractor referral service, or reputable cleaning service with bonded workers. If the service you require doesn't have an associated agency, you can check with a consumer ratings company such as Angie's List (online at www.angieslist.com) for recommendations.

Keep tabs on finances. Whether you pay bills yourself or hire a service to handle them for you, check credit card and bank statements and be alert for any possible problems or evidence of financial abuse.

Hire a geriatric care manager. An experienced local geriatric care manager can lift a large weight off your shoulders. He or she can help you plan and coordinate home care services swiftly and efficiently.

Assessing your loved one's needs

The questionnaire on the following pages can help you figure out your loved one's care needs, including household chores, medical assistance, or personal

▶ What is the Agency on Aging?

When you need guidance on anything from transportation to insurance benefits, turn to your local Agency on Aging. This network of federally funded senior assistance programs includes about 620 organizations in communities all over the country. Some are based in cities; others provide services county- or statewide. These programs may go by other names, such as the Office on Aging or the Aging and Disability Resource Center.

Your local agency can provide you with free

• caregiver training

• information about elder assistance programs and long-term care

• home-delivered meals and nutrition counseling

• insurance benefits counseling

• transportation

• help completing applications for assistance programs like Medicaid.

To find your local Agency on Aging or a similar service, visit www.n4a.org and search by your city and state or ZIP code; or call 800-677-1116 (toll-free).

Caring for someone difficult

Caregiving can be a rewarding experience, particularly if the person you're caring for nurtured you through your early years. What better way to give back? But what if you had a strained relationship with the person, or he or she was abusive in the past? Or, what if your loved one has suddenly become hard to deal with? Even people who were kind and easygoing early in life can become difficult and demanding with age or disability.

Depending on the relationship you've had with this person, you may be torn about serving as caregiver. Don't feel guilty if you decide to bow out or hand over part of the responsibilities. You have the right to say no if the prospect of caregiving makes you feel uncomfortable.

If you do decide to move forward, don't try to embark on this process alone. Line up siblings or other relatives to help you, or just to lend an ear when you need to vent. Also consider hiring a geriatric care manager to shoulder some of the care burden (see "Consulting a geriatric care manager," page 6).

Anticipate problems that might arise while you're caring for the person, and plan your response to them. For example, if you know that your parent will react angrily to your cooking, set up clear expectations and establish boundaries

to prevent a big blowup. For example, you might say, "I'm going to be cooking meals for the week and freezing them. Here is a list of the foods I can make. Which ones would you prefer?" You can also ask a therapist or counselor for advice on handling conflicts.

Take time to nurture yourself throughout this process. Schedule breaks throughout the week for you to get away and tend to your own needs. If the difficult behavior becomes too much for you to bear, consider calling in professional help to relieve some of the burden on you.

care tasks like dressing and maintaining personal hygiene. It will also help you identify possible ways to fulfill those needs. Going through the questionnaire categories with your loved one may stimulate ideas, allow you to dismiss some preconceived notions, and guide you both toward the issues that require the most assistance. When filling out this questionnaire, it's helpful to speak with a variety of people, including the following:

• the primary caregiver (if it's not you)

• any doctors, social workers, or professionals involved in the person's care
• other people who are in a position to know about day-to-day needs, such as neighbors, friends, and relatives
• a geriatric care manager, if you're working with one (he or she may opt to use other professional assessment tools instead of this questionnaire).

Before filling out this questionnaire, make copies so you can use it again as circumstances change. ◆

THE NEEDS QUESTIONNAIRE

This questionnaire is designed to help you identify problematic areas and find possible solutions. All the questions apply to the care recipient and his or her surroundings.

The "Action steps" box in each section is a place for you to jot down things you can do to address any problems. For suggestions on managing problems with mobility, meals, bathing, dressing, and toilet use, see the chapter "Handling day-to-day issues," page 15.

Once you complete this form, you can bring it to a geriatrician or geriatric care manager for discussion. He or she can help you put together a comprehensive, personalized caregiving plan.

Household issues

MORNING ROUTINE	YES	NO
Is it difficult to get the person out of bed?		
Is it difficult to get the person dressed?		
Other related problems:		
Action steps:		

SHOPPING	YES	NO
Are there nutritious foods in the refrigerator and on kitchen shelves?		
Is food going bad?		
• If yes, is too much food being bought at one time?		
• Or is not enough food being eaten?		
Is shopping difficult for the person to manage?		
• If yes, who does the shopping?		
Other related problems:		
Action steps:		

CLOTHES AND DRESSING	YES	NO
Are clothes clean and in good repair?		
Is it easy for the person to do the laundry?		
Are clothes easy to get on and off?		
Is it easy to reach clothing in closets?		
Are the closets overly cluttered?		
Are clothes appropriate for the season?		
Other related problems:		
Action steps:		

MEALS	YES	NO
Is the person preparing and eating meals?		
• If yes, how frequently?		
• If not, who is primarily preparing meals?		
What do the person's typical meals consist of?		
Which foods does the person avoid because of allergies, intolerance, or discomfort?		
Does the person take a daily multivitamin?		
Has the person lost or gained a significant amount of weight in the past month?		
Are dental problems, difficulty shopping, loneliness, money, or other concerns interfering with healthy eating?		
• If yes, which problems are affecting eating?		
Is difficulty using the stove or reading dials, packaging, or cookbooks interfering with healthy eating?		
Is the kitchen accessible?		
Are frequently used pots, foods, and other items easy to reach?		
Are cabinets and drawers easy to open?		
Are kitchen tools easy to use?		
Other related problems:		
Action steps:		

Continued

Household issues

BATHING AND TOILET USE	YES	NO
Are any of these personal care tasks an issue?		
• Bathing		
• Combing hair		
• Brushing teeth		
• Controlling body odor		
Is the tub or shower easy to get into and out of?		
Is standing or balancing a problem?		
• If yes, would the person be more comfortable using a shower seat?		
Does the bathroom have nonslip surfaces to minimize the risk of falls?		
Are grab bars installed in the tub or shower and near the toilet?		
Is it easy to get to a toilet when necessary?		
Do "accidents" ever occur?		
• If yes, how frequently?		
• Has a doctor investigated the incontinence issues?		
• Are incontinence products available and accessible?		
Is it easy to sit down on and rise from the toilet?		
Other related problems:		
Action steps:		

ACTIVITY AND MOBILITY	YES	NO
Does the person leave the house regularly?		
• Alone or accompanied? How often?		
Does the person drive?		
• If yes, do you think he or she is safe to drive?		
Can he or she safely use public transportation?		
Can he or she call a cab or request a pickup from Uber or Lyft?		
Are mobility problems making it difficult to get out?		
Is it easy to move around the apartment or house?		
Is going up and down stairs becoming difficult or dangerous?		
Is the person getting regular exercise?		
• What type(s) of exercise, and how much?		
Other related problems:		
Action steps:		

YARD AND WALKWAYS	YES	NO
Is yard work such as raking and mowing being kept up?		
If it snows, is there someone reliable available to shovel the walk or plow the driveway?		
• If yes, who?		
Other related problems:		
Action steps:		

SAFETY	YES	NO
Is the home safe inside and out?		
Are there falling hazards? (See "Preventing a fall," page 15.)		
Are working smoke detectors installed throughout the home?		
• If yes, are batteries replaced regularly?		
Is there sufficient lighting, especially at the entryway, on stairs, and in hallways?		
Is the home securely locked?		
Is there an accessible peephole for viewing visitors?		
Is the home sufficiently warm, but not too warm?		
Is heating safe? (For example, using the stove for extra heat is unsafe.)		
Is it cool enough on hot days?		
Does a neighbor have an extra key, or is one well-hidden near the home so people can enter in an emergency?		
Can the person easily hear, see, and reach the phone?		
Are emergency numbers (including neighbors, family, and doctors) posted near the phone in large, dark letters or entered into speed dial?		
Is an emergency plan in place?		
Does the person need a medical alert system such as Lifeline that summons help with the push of a button?		
Does the person compromise his or her own safety (for example, by forgetting a pot on a lit burner or smoking cigarettes while drowsy)?		
Who would notice and quickly summon help if, for example, the person fell or became ill?		
Other related problems:		
Action steps:		

Continued

Household issues

HOUSECLEANING AND UPKEEP	YES	NO
Is the home clean?		
Is it so cluttered as to be potentially unsafe?		
Are certain aspects of housecleaning or upkeep becoming too difficult to do?		
• If yes, which aspects?		
Are home repairs needed to improve safety?		
• If yes, which repairs?		
Other related problems:		
Action steps:		

MONEY	YES	NO
Are bills being paid on time?		
• If no, are finances a problem?		
• Is confusion a problem?		
Are bank and investment accounts in order?		
Are there any signs of financial abuse by unscrupulous home repair outfits, financial "advisers," paid caregivers, or others who prey on the elderly (for example, large amounts of money being withdrawn or sudden changes in money management)?		
Other related problems:		
Action steps:		

Medical issues

DOCTORS	YES	NO
Are health problems under control?		
• If no, what additional steps need to be taken?		
Are vision and hearing checked regularly?		
Does the person see a dentist regularly?		
Does the person see multiple doctors?		
• If yes, how many?		
Does one doctor coordinate treatment?		
Should a geriatrician be consulted (for example, if your loved one is dealing with late-life issues such as frequent falls or incontinence)?		
Is transportation to doctors' appointments needed?		
Are family members aware of health issues and medical care?		
Are there any signs of untreated health problems, sores, bruises, or falls?		
Has a health care proxy been appointed?		
• Have advance directives that spell out his or her goals for care been completed?		
• Has he or she completed a do-not-resuscitate order?		
• If so, is the form posted somewhere in the home?		
Other related problems:		
Action steps:		

FALLING	YES	NO
Has the person fallen?		
• If yes, where and when?		
Has the person been evaluated by his or her physician for this problem?		
Other related problems:		
Action steps:		

Continued

Medical issues

MEDICATIONS	YES	NO
How many prescription medications does the person take?		
How many over-the-counter medications does he or she take?		
Does the person have a chart, pill organizer, or other reminder system that makes it easier to take pills on time?		
Is an up-to-date list of medications posted in the house and carried in the person's purse or wallet?		
Are there problems with drug side effects?		
• Dizziness, drowsiness, or confusion?		
• Troublesome changes in behavior or appetite?		
• Problems with urination or bowel movements?		
• Other side effects?		
Has a doctor who coordinates care checked all the prescriptions at a recent visit?		
Are specialists kept aware of all medications taken?		
Are there signs that medications aren't being taken properly (too many or too few pills left in the bottle, outdated prescriptions)?		
Where are the prescriptions filled?		
Who picks up the prescriptions?		
Can the person afford all prescribed medications?		

Other related problems:

Action steps:

ALCOHOL OR SUBSTANCE ABUSE	YES	NO
Are there any signs of alcohol abuse or misuse of prescription drugs, such as confusion, falling, odors, or personality changes?		
Is the person aware of the importance of not mixing alcohol with certain medications?		

Other related problems:

Action steps:

CONFUSION, DEPRESSION, DEMENTIA	YES	NO
Are there signs of confusion or increasing forgetfulness?		
Has the person been found wandering or gotten lost in familiar places?		
Have personality changes occurred?		
Is anxiety, frustration, or rage increasingly a problem?		
Is the person staying home more than usual?		
Are there signs of depression, such as marked sadness, loss of interest in previously enjoyed activities and friends, or significant changes in appetite, grooming, or sleep?		

Other related problems:

Action steps:

EMOTIONAL NEEDS	YES	NO
Does the person seem to feel vital and connected?		
Does he or she keep up with friends or regularly engage in social activities?		
Is loneliness or boredom an issue?		
Have there been significant losses—a spouse or close friend—in the last year or so?		
If isolation is a problem, could one of the following be interfering with social activities:		
• Transportation		
• Mobility		
• Poor hearing		
• Loss of friends due to death or relocation		

Other related problems:

Action steps:

GENERAL OBSERVATIONS (USE A SEPARATE SHEET OF PAPER)
What are the concerns of the person needing care?
What are your concerns about the current situation?
What are the goals of care?

Handling day-to-day issues

Caregiving revolves around daily tasks. Perhaps the person you care for is able to take full responsibility for many activities but needs a helping hand with things like dressing or preparing meals. Or maybe the recipient needs constant assistance—for example, if your loved one has Alzheimer's or Parkinson's disease—and your role is therefore more challenging. Here are tips to help you make some of the most basic caregiving duties a little easier.

Getting around

Restoring or maintaining a person's mobility, both inside and outside the home, improves independence. It provides a change of scenery and puts a visit to the mall or a walk with friends back within reach. This in turn lifts the person's spirits and takes some of the burden off the caregiver.

Begin by asking the person's doctor for advice. (If you can't come to appointments with your loved one, ask to be put on speakerphone so you can raise

Helpful devices and products

A number of companies sell mobility and accessibility devices, from canes and walkers to easy-to-use household gadgets like book magnifiers and jar openers. You can do a Google search for the product you need, or check with one of these two online companies, which offer a broad range of products on their websites.

Assisted Living Store, Inc.
199 Bridgepoint Drive
South St. Paul, MN 55075
888-388-5862 (toll-free)
www.assistedlivingstore.com

Independent Living Aids
137 Rano Road
Buffalo, NY 14207
800-537-2118 (toll-free)
www.independentliving.com (also offers a printed catalog)

Did you know? | More than one-fifth of the 43 million unpaid caregivers in the United States care for someone with Alzheimer's disease or another form of dementia.
Source: Caregiving in the U.S. 2015.

important issues during the visit.) For instance, would it help for the person to start an exercise program or get better control over a medical condition? Would it help for him or her to use an assistive device, such as a cane, walker, or wheelchair? So many types of devices are available today that the choices can be overwhelming. To find out which one is most appropriate, the doctor can refer you to a skilled physical therapist who can provide an evaluation, order the right equipment, and teach your loved one how to use it. Insurance will pay for most assistive devices if a physician prescribes them or a physical therapist recommends them.

In addition, ask the doctor whether medications may be interfering with mobility. For example, are medications making the person dizzy or tired? If so, could any changes be made to the drug regimen? Perhaps untreated or inadequately treated pain is the issue. Finally, find out how a debilitating condition might progress so you can prepare for any future changes in mobility.

Preventing a fall

Falls are the leading cause of hip fractures, traumatic brain injuries, and other serious injuries among older adults. Many older adults are so fearful of falling that they actually shy away from walking, regular exercise, and enjoyable activities. This cautious approach is in fact very harmful, as immobility weakens muscles and bones, further increasing the person's vulnerability to falls and fractures.

Fortunately, you can take many steps to prevent

falls, from safety-proofing the home to incorporating strength-training exercises.

Identify trouble spots. Clear away clutter and items like loose wires, cords, and throw rugs. Check that stairs are sturdy, with strong railings. Make sure stairways, entrances, and walkways are well lit. Equip bedrooms, bathrooms, and hallways with night lights. Install motion-sensitive lights that turn on when a person enters a room. Place glow-in-the-dark light switches at each doorway.

Invest in safety equipment. Install grab bars in the shower or tub, and put nonskid mats on bathroom floors. A shower chair can be helpful, too. If getting on and off the toilet is difficult, install a raised toilet seat with arms. In the kitchen and other areas of the house, store frequently used items in easy-to-reach cabinets. Provide a grasping tool for accessing out-of-reach items; it's safer than standing on a chair or stepladder. See a doctor and physical therapist to determine the person's need for a cane or walker.

Pay attention to health. Regular eye exams and proper eyewear greatly reduce the risk of falls. Flat rubber-soled shoes improve balance and offer greater traction. Limiting or avoiding alcohol can also help with steadiness. Talk with the doctor about any medications that might impair the person's balance, as well as illnesses that can affect the inner ear and cause dizziness.

Increase strength and flexibility. Numerous studies show that strengthening muscles and improving flexibility and coordination enhance balance at every age. Better balance leads to fewer falls and makes it easier to participate in other activities. Simple balance exercises and gentle programs like yoga or tai chi, performed daily, can do wonders for both mind and body.

Meals

Having meals together is a wonderful way to share time with your loved one. Take steps to ensure that the kitchen is safe, provide nutritious meals, and encourage the person to eat.

Preparation

Home-cooked meals are almost always more appealing and nutritious than commercially prepared or packaged foods. Cooking at home also offers an opportunity for the care recipient to participate in meal preparation. Try the following tips to make meals easier for both of you.

- Make and freeze portion-sized meals or soups to microwave later. (This is a task you can delegate to family members or friends who want to help.)
- Peruse the Internet for healthy recipes that are low in sodium and high in nutrients. You'll find hundreds of great ideas for quick and easy meals, with nutritional information included.
- Make the kitchen accessible by ensuring that key items are within easy reach. Products designed to compensate for disabilities, such as large-print cookbooks, jar openers, and easy-to-open food containers, can simplify cooking.
- Offer to do the shopping for heavy items, like canned goods or milk. You can also buy groceries online or by phone and have them delivered. (Just make sure someone is available to help put away groceries if the person is unable to do so alone.)
- If cooking is too much for you, look for a local meal delivery service, such as Meals on Wheels America (www.mealsonwheelsamerica.org). Personal Chef To Go (www.personalcheftogo.com) and Magic Kitchen (www.magickitchen.com) will also deliver full, nutritionally balanced meals to your loved one.
- If the person you're caring for dislikes eating alone, arrange dinner and lunch dates. Be on hand yourself when possible. Some senior centers and other organizations offer group dining. Mealtimes are important opportunities for social contact. Moreover, people who eat meals alone often don't eat enough.

When eating habits change

Appetite and weight changes are common early signs

▶ **Consider kitchen safety**

If confusion is a problem for your loved one, make sure the burners on the stove are covered and can't be turned on (see "Caring for a person with dementia," page 20). Also remove other household appliances, like toaster ovens and microwaves, that might be dangerous. Microwaves, for example, can cause steam burns.

of physical, mental, or emotional problems. If you notice that your loved one has unintentionally lost weight, check with a doctor to determine why. If poor eating is an issue, try to improve the person's appetite by using more spices to enhance flavors and by preparing his or her favorite dishes. Incorporate nutritional supplements like Ensure Plus or Boost if the person isn't eating enough. Also talk to a nutritionist, who may be able to help you develop meals that not only are appealing but also address health issues and dietary restrictions. A nutritionist may also be able to rework old favorite recipes to meet current health concerns.

Consider whether dental problems may be to blame for changes in eating. Softer foods (scrambled eggs, oatmeal, or even baby foods) and small meals or frequent healthy snacks may make eating easier. A trip to the dentist is in order if ill-fitting dentures or mouth pain might be causing changes in eating habits that are contributing to weight loss.

Alzheimer's disease and other forms of dementia can affect eating habits as well. As these illnesses progress, a person may find it harder to remember to eat and may need prompts and encouragement.

Personal hygiene

Dirty clothes, unkempt hair, and other slips in personal hygiene may be a sign of limited energy or abilities. Sometimes they point to bigger issues, such as depression, hidden health problems, or the beginning of dementia or cognitive decline.

Talk with a doctor if you notice significant problems with your loved one's personal hygiene. Neuropsychological testing may be the next step to determine whether this is an early sign of cognitive problems. The doctor may also want to rule out depression, in which case effective treatments are available. Some-

times the change stems from a lack of energy, which may be due to poor nutrition, trouble sleeping, progression of a chronic medical problem, or a new health concern, such as anemia or a thyroid disorder. In other cases, medications may be at fault. The doctor can sort through possible causes and help you determine how to address the problem. The tips below can help with some of the practical aspects of personal hygiene.

Bathing

A surprising number of obstacles can make regular bathing difficult, including arthritis, balance problems, mental confusion (see "Caring for a person with dementia," page 20), or a loss of physical ability from stroke or injury. Once you've assessed the cause, try to address it through a variety of approaches. Consider these issues:

Is the tub or shower accessible? If not, install grab bars, which can make it easier to get into and out of the shower or tub. If the person has trouble standing or balancing, a handheld nozzle positioned at chest height and a shower seat can make it possible to shower while seated. In some cases, it's worthwhile to install a walk-in tub, or a shower with a built-in seat and a wide, flat entry designed for wheelchair or walker access.

Is the tub or shower safe? Put nonslip decals or a bath mat in the tub. On the floor, consider using textured tiles, which tend to be less slippery when wet. Make sure that all bath rugs are absorbent and nonslip

A few simple home changes may allow a person to live independently at home longer. For example, adding grab bars, a shower seat, a nonslip bath mat, and an elevated toilet seat to the bathroom can make it safer and easier to maneuver around.

to avoid falls when the person leaves the tub or shower.

Is the person always cold? If so, he or she may feel too chilly to bathe. Poor circulation or a thyroid condition can contribute to chills. Talk with a doctor about these and other possible health-related causes. The ability to regulate internal temperature diminishes with age. Try heating the bathroom beforehand using properly installed heat lights or a portable radiator (but make sure they're turned off after each use). Have large towels or a thick terry robe warmed in the dryer or on a towel warming rack ready for when the person is done bathing. Or try sponge baths in a warm room.

Is shampooing or hair styling too difficult? A shorter cut can make drying and brushing easier. You might offer to shampoo the person's hair yourself, or arrange for regular visits to a hairdresser. Some stylists make home visits.

Is the person afraid of bathing? People with dementia can develop a fear of bathing that leads to agitation during showers or baths. To calm any fears, play soothing music or talk about something enjoyable as a distraction. Cut down on bathing (for example, go from daily showers to twice weekly), or substitute sponge baths if worries over taking a shower or tub bath are insurmountable.

Dressing

Clothes should be comfortable and easy to wear and wash, yet still allow for personal style. Clothing and shoes should be made from breathable materials that encourage airflow and reduce sweating. Arthritis or dementia may make it hard to negotiate buttons, zippers, or snaps. Soft sweaters, skirts or pants with Velcro closures or elastic waistbands, long-sleeve or short-sleeve T-shirts, and "athleisure" wear are often better choices. Choose shoes that slip on or have Velcro fasteners or elastic laces.

If it is hard for a person to grip items or bend, purchase products that help with pulling on clothes, such as a dressing stick, shoehorn, or sock helper. See an occupational therapist for more recommendations and training on the use of these accessories.

Clothes designed for older or disabled people are sometimes undignified, or dreary and dull. If the per-

The power of music

We all have favorite songs that stir up old memories and take us straight back to a special time and place in our lives, such as a high school prom or a romantic trip to Italy. Researchers are finding that the cognitive response to music is so strong that, even in a person with late-stage dementia, the right song can bring up lost memories and restore a connection to the world. (So, by the way, can watching old movies.)

To evoke the greatest response, experts recommend playing your loved one's favorite songs from his or her young adult years—ages 18 to 25. Choose songs that are appropriate to the activity. If you want to the person to be alert, such as for bathing and dressing, turn on an up-tempo song. When it's time to calm down, put on a slow ballad. Experiment with different songs until you find a selection of tunes that elicit the right responses.

son you care for was a sharp dresser or enjoyed bright colors, encourage him or her to continue with those preferences. Shop for favorite styles in a catalog or online if it's hard for the person to leave the house.

Dental care

Good dental care is essential but often neglected. That's because many older adults do not have dental insurance and must pay out of pocket for all dental services. (Medicare Part B doesn't cover most dental care, and less than half of states provide it to their Medicaid recipients. However, many Medicare Advantage plans do offer dental coverage. See "Navigating Medicare and Medicaid," page 32.) To prevent oral health issues from causing tooth decay and health problems in general, be aware of the following:

- Poor nutrition sometimes stems from trouble chewing, difficulty swallowing due to too little saliva, or ill-fitting dentures that work poorly or hurt. If you notice that your care recipient is not eating enough, one of these issues may be the cause.
- Gum inflammation (gingivitis) and advanced gum disease (periodontitis) are important to address, because they could have much broader health implications. Increasing evidence links gum disease to diabetes and heart disease.
- Routine dental check-ups and professional cleanings

are important. So are flossing, proper brushing of the teeth and tongue, and regular denture cleanings. Rinsing twice daily with antiseptic mouthwash may help reduce plaque buildup and gum inflammation.

- If your loved one has trouble gripping a toothbrush, choose one designed to accommodate a weak grip, or try padding or lengthening the handle yourself. An electric toothbrush may also be easier to use.
- Certain medications and medical treatments, and possibly aging itself, can make saliva flow less freely than normal. This affects tooth and gum health and can cause bad breath. Artificial saliva products, sugarless gum, hard candies (especially sour flavors), frequent sips of water, and avoidance of caffeine, alcohol, and tobacco can help relieve dry mouth.

Using the toilet

Make sure clothes are easy to slip off when nature calls. If it's hard for the person to get to the bathroom quickly—especially at night—purchase a bedside commode or handheld urinal. Check that the path to the bathroom is always kept clear and well lit. Keep a night light on in the bathroom, too.

If sitting down and getting up is a problem, install grab bars and an elevated toilet seat or a base that raises a standard toilet several inches. Keep wet wipes close to the toilet for comfort and hygiene (see "Incontinence," above right).

Incontinence

Incontinence can become a significant problem with age and illness. It can make personal hygiene difficult, which in turn can make socializing a challenge because of the odor and embarrassment involved. If not handled properly, incontinence could also pose a threat to your loved one's health.

Urinary incontinence

Occasional urine leaks are a normal, if unpleasant, part of growing older. Yet for some people, the problem is significant enough to disrupt their daily activities and hygiene. Loss of control over urination—called urinary incontinence—isn't a normal part of aging. The underlying causes just become more common as we get older. It's important to investigate the root problem, because proper treatment can help.

Watch for clues like smells or stains, since people may be too embarrassed to reveal they have incontinence. If you suspect a problem, reassure the person that urine leakage is a medical symptom that deserves the same attention and care as any other medical problem.

A doctor can help determine what kind of incontinence the person has, and what's causing it. You may need to consult a gynecologist or urogynecologist (for women), urologist (for men), or geriatrician. Many treatments are available, including pelvic floor

How to change an adult diaper

If you raised children, you probably became accustomed to diaper changes. Yet changing a full-grown adult can much more challenging than changing a baby, given their size and the potential embarrassment involved.

Follow these steps to make diaper changes easier and more pleasant for you and the person you're caring for:

- Place all the supplies you'll need close by, including a clean diaper, wet wipes, barrier cream or ointment, trashcan or diaper disposal unit, and one or more towels.
- The ideal place to change an adult is on the bed, but if you can't lift the person, the floor is also acceptable.
- Place a towel beneath his or her lower body for comfort and cleanliness.
- Take off the pants or skirt—don't just pull them down (use

a towel as a cover-up for purposes of modesty).
- Undo the diaper tapes and open up the diaper.
- Pull the person's knees up to his or her chest so you can clean the person. Wipe from front to back, especially for women. This will ensure no bacteria spread from the rectum to the vagina.
- Using your free hand, fold up the diaper and put it into the trashcan.
- Place the clean diaper under the person. It should reach a couple of inches above the tailbone in the back.
- Lay the person down on the diaper. Apply ointment, if needed.
- Pull the diaper up between the legs. Close it snugly and fasten it on each side. Help to dress the person again.

exercises, bladder training, medication, catheters, and surgery. Sometimes all that's needed is a change of medication, easier-to-open clothing, or a more accessible toilet.

The treatment for incontinence depends on the cause. While a doctor should determine the best approach, the following simple strategies may also prove helpful.

- When you're out in public, scout bathrooms and stay close to them for quick access. At home, keep a commode next to the bed if the bathroom is too far away or if mobility problems make it hard to reach quickly.

- Make sure clothes are easy to remove.
- Try scheduling bathroom visits every hour or two. If the person is bedridden, schedule bedpans at set intervals.
- Limit caffeine and alcohol. But offer regular amounts of water and other fluids, since dehydration can irritate the bladder and aggravate incontinence. You only need to limit fluids within three hours before bedtime to prevent the need for overnight bathroom visits.
- Be alert to signs of a urinary tract infection, such as a frequent need to urinate, an unusual odor or

Caring for a person with dementia

The daily routine can become more challenging when the person you are caring for is mentally confused because of Alzheimer's disease or another form of dementia. More than half of family members caring for someone with dementia felt they were "on duty" 24 hours a day, according to a report in *The New England Journal of Medicine*. In these cases, ensuring the person's safety can be difficult. Abilities typically wax and wane from day to day and even from hour to hour. "Sundowning"—increased confusion that becomes more apparent as night approaches—is common, too.

Some of the general suggestions listed in this report can help with daily tasks. Below are a few additional tips for people who care for individuals with dementia. Adjust them as necessary to accommodate your loved one's personality and stage of disease.

Communicate clearly. Use simple phrasing and short sentences to explain what needs to be done, but be careful to avoid talking to the person as if he or she were a child. Also, try to be patient. Allow ample time for him or her to respond or complete a task. Try not to interrupt. Put important reminders or information in writing for easy reference.

Modify mealtime routines. Stick to a calm, simple mealtime routine. Encourage the person to use the bathroom beforehand. Eliminate distractions and limit choices by offering one food at a time with the right utensil. Keep eating areas well lit and use plates that contrast with the food for better visibility. Cut food into small pieces. Switch to softer foods like applesauce, ice cream, or pureed vegetables if the person chokes easily or often forgets to chew. Curved spoons, plates that are divided or have high sides, and straws can make it easier for a person to feed himself or herself. If eating is a messy endeavor, put down a wipe-off tablecloth, use spill-proof cups, and offer an apron or bib to keep clothes clean. Watch for weight loss and dehydration, which are common among people with dementia.

Document toilet use. Keep a record of when the person urinates and has bowel movements, and remind him or her to use the bathroom at regular intervals. Restlessness or agitation may indicate a full bladder or the need to have a bowel movement. If the person has trouble urinating, have him or her blow bubbles through a straw in a glass of water, turn on the tap, or put on some soothing music. It may be easier to go while in a relaxed state.

Establish a bathing routine. A fear of bathing often arises during the middle stages of Alzheimer's, possibly in response to faltering motor skills and an inability to process information. It's important to set a bathing routine that closely mimics what your loved one used to do, and stick with it. Before bringing him or her to the bathroom, lay out everything—including towel, soap, and bathrobe or clothes—and fill the tub or start the shower. Be gentle, calm, and reassuring while talking through the steps of the bath or shower one by one. Short, gentle phrases help. Respect modesty by covering portions of the person's body with a towel, but never leave your loved one alone in the tub. If the person resists bathing or becomes agitated, stop and try again later when he or she is in a good mood.

Bathing is a good time to check for rashes, reddened skin, or sores, so these problems can be treated before they get worse. Applying cornstarch to the skin after a bath can help minimize chafing; baking soda also helps and has deodorizing properties.

Choose easy, comfortable clothes. Articles of clothing with elastic waists rather than potentially confusing buttons, hooks, snaps, and ties prevent stress and encourage self-dependence. Lay out clothes in the order in which they should be put on. Encourage simple choices, but cut down on the number of clothing options if this seems to upset the person.

Adjust activities to ability. It's important to keep a person with dementia engaged and stimulated, but as abilities change, some once-favorite activities may become too difficult. Try not

color to the urine, pain or blood when urinating, and fever. Discuss these symptoms with the person's doctor.

- Help your loved one stay dry by providing absorbent pads, diapers, or underwear (see "How to change an adult diaper," page 19). For women, absorbent underwear includes a special crotch that wicks urine away from the skin and stores it. For men, there are drip shields (with light protection) and guards (with heavier protection) that have waterproof backings and are designed for the male anatomy. If you use pads, choose a product that incorporates superabsorbent layers to pull fluid into the core of the pad, away from the skin. Encourage the person to use the bathroom often and change pads, diapers, or underwear frequently. And keep a container handy for soiled clothes.

- In addition to using absorbent products, clean any skin that comes in contact with urine. Urine is acidic and can irritate the skin, causing rashes and sores. Provide moist wipes to clean the skin in the affected area. Apply a barrier cream or ointment such as Vaseline when changing pads, diapers, or underwear. Avoid products like A&D or Bacitra-

to abandon all hobbies and beloved rituals. Sometimes adjusting the activity helps. For example, if you know your loved one can no longer read and understand the newspaper, he or she still might find pleasure in the physical act of holding the paper, turning its pages, and looking at pictures and print. Or if movies were a favorite pastime, try going to children's films, which are designed for people with shorter attention spans. Sit near the aisle and be prepared to leave early if necessary. At home, listen to music or audiobooks, or color in adult coloring books for relaxation.

Prevent wandering. Wandering is a dangerous, distressing problem. Often, it's the main reason a family has to place a loved one in a nursing home. If your family member or friend is still living at home or is living with you, you can take measures to prevent wandering and protect the individual if he or she does roam. For example:

- Install door locks that are difficult for a person with dementia to see or open, such as a latch near the top of the door.

- Place gates at stairwells to prevent falls.

- Provide a place for the person to wander safely, such as a path through the home or a circular trail through a fenced backyard.

- Install alarms on doors to alert you when the individual is on the move.

- Purchase a wandering prevention device like SafeWander (www.safewander.com). It consists of a wearable sensor that sends a message to the caregiver's smartphone when the wearer gets out of bed.

- Camouflage doors with paint or wallpaper that matches the surrounding walls. A mirror or stop sign on the door might help as well.

If the person does wander off, an identification bracelet can help get him or her home safely. Engrave the bracelet with "memory impaired" as well as the person's name, address, and phone number. Be sure that the bracelet is too small to slip off the wrist, and is securely fastened. The Alzheimer's Association and MedicAlert jointly offer a national program called Safe Return, with a 24-hour emergency response line to locate lost people (www.medicalert.org/safereturn). There is a $55 fee for the bracelet and a $35 annual fee for the service.

Eliminate household hazards. Remove and hide stove knobs so burners cannot be turned on. With electric stoves, install a switch that inactivates burners, or keep the stove switched off at the fuse box or circuit breaker. Ask the local gas company for more suggestions on disabling gas stoves. Store poisonous substances, cleaning supplies, gasoline, paint, solvents, and medicines in cabinets with locks or childproof latches. Lock up firearms, power tools, and machinery or remove them from the home. Lower water heater temperatures, insulate any exposed hot-water pipes, block off radiators with furniture or a gate, and take measures to prevent falls (see "Preventing a fall," page 15).

Manage cognitive limitations without upsetting the person. While physical safety is an important consideration, so are your loved one's emotional needs. Maintaining a routine, as described above, helps a person feel secure. What you say to the person is also important, if quickly forgotten. When he or she reaches the stage of advanced dementia, it's counterproductive to insist on a true version of events all the time. Instead, use "lie-lets," or little lies, that are more consistent with your loved one's beliefs. If your loved one is upset that she hasn't heard from her sister lately—a sister who died years before—don't respond by saying, "Don't you remember? Mabel died eight years ago." Instead, say that she's on vacation and will call when she gets back. This will calm your loved one, and most of the time he or she will completely forget the conversation.

Treating constipation and diarrhea

If constipation or diarrhea is a consistent issue, discuss it with a doctor who can make a proper diagnosis and suggest the appropriate treatment. Your loved one can also try the following tips.

For constipation:

- Add fiber to the diet. (Good sources include bran cereals, whole-grain breads, and uncooked fruits and vegetables, unless the person has swallowing problems or dental issues that make these unwise choices.)
- Take fiber supplements such as psyllium powder (Metamucil or Konsyl, for example) or methylcellulose.
- Drink more water or other fluids.
- Exercise as often as possible.
- Try a stool softener, but don't overdo it. Using stool softeners too often can reduce the absorption of nutrients, leading to deficiencies.

- Use the toilet when the urge strikes, rather than trying to hold back. Getting into a regular toilet routine may help, too.

For diarrhea:

- Get more soluble fiber in the diet. Pectin in blueberries or other fruits can help produce firmer stools.
- Wash produce well before eating it to avoid any bacterial contamination.
- Eliminate foods that can lead to loose stools, such as caffeinated beverages, cured or smoked meats, spicy foods, alcohol, dairy products, sweeteners (particularly sorbitol, mannitol, and xylitol), and fatty and greasy foods.
- If dairy products frequently trigger diarrhea, try lactase tablets or lactose-reduced or lactose-free products.
- During a bout of diarrhea, try kaolin and pectin (Kaopectate).

- Ask the doctor or pharmacist if any medications the person takes cause diarrhea as a side effect. If so, check into alternatives.
- Make sure a portable commode is handy if it's hard to reach the bathroom quickly.
- Drink plenty of water or other clear liquids. Diarrhea can cause dehydration—a serious health problem. It may help to have liquids 30 minutes before or after meals rather than with meals, since fluid speeds the passage of food through the digestive tract.
- After a bout of diarrhea, people often have little desire to eat for a day or so. When you begin eating again, start back with a BRAT diet: bananas, rice, applesauce, and white toast. Bananas bind the stool, while white rice, applesauce, and dry, white toast are low in fiber and easily digested.

cin, which can further irritate the skin. Immediately treat any sores that do appear. If necessary, contact a doctor for advice.

- Waterproof liners on beds or furniture can prevent stains and odors in the event of accidents.

Bowel incontinence

Bowel (fecal) incontinence is perceived as rare because people are often reluctant to seek help for it. Yet it affects 15% of older women and up to 10% of men. Bowel incontinence places undeniable stress on an individual and his or her caregivers, and is often a primary reason for nursing home placement. In some cases, though, the problem can be solved with far less drastic measures.

If your loved one is experiencing bowel incontinence, contact a doctor, who can sort out the possible causes and recommend treatment. Often, the underlying problem is constipation or diarrhea (see "Treating constipation and diarrhea," above). When stool obstructs the bowel, some can leak around the block-

age. Diarrhea has the opposite effect and may make it hard to get to the bathroom in time.

Increasing fiber in the diet often helps. A lack of fiber slows movement of food through the bowel. Fiber improves bowel control by making the stool larger, softer, and less watery. Having a daily serving of bran cereal or taking psyllium fiber supplements with plenty of water can help with fecal incontinence.

Exercise also relieves constipation by helping food move through the intestines more efficiently. Encourage the person in your care to walk or do other aerobic exercises every day, if health permits.

Medications can also contribute to diarrhea and constipation. Sometimes, a health condition or injury may be to blame. Investigate these potential causes so they can be treated.

When accidents occur, try to be calm and understanding. If the person wears diapers, keep the area clean—including under any body folds (see "How to change an adult diaper," page 19). Use an ointment at each change to prevent rashes. ◥

Legal planning

What does legal planning have to do with a family member's health care? Quite a bit. It can help ensure that a person's wishes for handling finances, medical decisions, and end-of-life care are followed. Some of these topics are very hard to talk about, but avoiding them will almost always create problems later on. Whenever possible, discuss legal issues while a person is still capable of handling his or her own affairs, long before you're in the midst of a medical crisis.

Confronting end-of-life concerns: A crucial first step

Most people facing the end of life are forced to confront many issues: grief, regret, worry about their legacy, loss of autonomy, and concerns about the family members and friends they will leave behind. To respect your loved one's values and beliefs and properly carry out his or her wishes, it's imperative that you have a series of conversations about the person's wishes and goals. It's extremely important that you start the formal process while he or she is still able to participate in the conversations and planning. It may also be helpful to talk to a religious adviser about spiritual concerns. Below are some specific questions you should ask your care recipient.

- Who do you want to make financial decisions for you if you are no longer able to make your own choices?
- Who do you want to make health care decisions for you if you are no longer able to make your own choices? (It will not necessarily be the same person who makes your financial decisions.)
- What are your main goals, should you become terminally ill? What trade-offs between length of life and quality of life are you willing to make? (For example, do you want to live as long as possible under any circumstances, or do you want to suffer as little as possible, if you have no chance of recovery?)

- Are there medical conditions under which you would not wish to be resuscitated when you stop breathing or your heart stops? (Heroic measures and life support can be traumatic.)
- Do you want to be hospitalized, or stay at home or somewhere else, if you are seriously or terminally ill?
- How will you pay for care? Do you have adequate insurance or other funding sources? What costs might arise while your loved ones are caring for you or grieving?
- Will your loved ones be prepared for the decisions they may have to make upon your death?

This chapter and those that follow outline the legal documents, care directives, and other information you'll need to take control of the planning process.

Wills and trusts

Wills and trusts are legal documents that enable people to distribute their assets and belongings as they see fit. Detailed information on wills and trusts is beyond the scope of this report; however, a few major

Every adult should have a will and a health care power of attorney. It's especially important for a person receiving caregiving to complete these documents, along with a durable power of attorney, while he or she is still able to do so.

differences between the two are outlined below.

A will is a document that outlines how the person wants his or her property—including home, car, and other valuables—to be distributed among children and other loved ones. Wishes relayed through a will take effect only after a person's death. Also, wills go through a public legal process called probate unless the value of the estate is below an amount set by the state. Probate helps ensure that heirs and creditors are notified of the death, that the person had the right to give away assets described in the will, and that all assets go to the right people. This process can be lengthy and costly.

A trust is an agreement that allows an individual (the grantor or settlor) to split the ownership of property between a trustee (whose sole job is to manage the property according to the terms of the trust) and the beneficiaries (those who are intended to benefit from the property now or in the future). There are many kinds of trusts, but a common distinction is made between those that go into effect during the grantor's lifetime (living trusts) and those that go into effect after the grantor's death (testamentary trusts). Living trusts are sometimes used to plan for the possibility that a person may at some point be unable to handle his or her own finances. The individual puts property into the trust now and serves as trustee for his or her own benefit; but in the event of incapacity, a designated successor trustee takes over and manages the property for the benefit of the grantor. At the grantor's death, the property in the trust goes to whomever the grantor designated as a beneficiary.

Trusts can be costly to set up and may have implications for taxes and Medicaid planning that should be discussed with a lawyer who is experienced in estate planning. Whether the benefits of having a trust outweigh the costs hinges on many factors, including the size of the estate, the person's marital status, the number of children, the potential estate taxes, and whether there are other options for handling the assets involved.

Trusts are also used to supplement the income of disabled persons who need to qualify for public benefits such as Medicaid and Supplemental Security Income. These trusts may be set up as a supplemental needs trust (SNT) for an individual or as a "pooled trust" that combines the money of many persons with disabilities in order to maximize investment potential and efficiency of management.

Pooled trust funds are invested and managed as a single account, but each beneficiary has his or her own account within the trust, according to the amount contributed. Withdrawals from an SNT or from the beneficiary's portion of a pooled trust can be used

Finding the right attorney

It is vital for caregivers to find an attorney with the appropriate expertise. To help you plan for long-term care, look for an attorney who has knowledge of the following legal specialties:

- Medicaid laws and regulations
- Social Security
- trusts (special-needs trusts)
- guardianships and conservatorships
- durable power of attorney for health care (health care proxy)
- durable power of attorney for asset management
- tax (income, estate, and gift) planning

- housing and health care contracts.

Not every attorney has experience in all of the above-mentioned areas. Some people will need to hire more than one attorney to cover their needs.

One of the best ways to find an attorney specializing in elder law is through a personal recommendation from a friend, relative, or co-worker, or from another attorney you know and trust. Another way is to attend a caregiver support group and ask if anyone can recommend a knowledgeable attorney.

Your local area Agency on Aging or bar association may provide referrals to attorneys in your area. You might also find help through the National Academy of Elder Law Attorneys (NAELA; see "Resources," page 52). Initial consultations generally cost a nominal fee. However, exercise caution when using a lawyer referral service, usually sponsored by state or local bar associations. Attorneys who participate in these referral services must meet only minimum requirements and may have little experience. It's important to check an attorney's qualifications and call several lawyers to compare their fees and experience.

to pay for services not covered by Medicaid or other insurance—for example, geriatric care services, extra nursing care, and the cost difference between a shared or private room in a nursing home. Funds can also cover the costs of eyeglasses, incontinence supplies, guardian fees, and insurance premiums. Typically, much less money is required to enroll in a pooled trust than would be necessary to set up an individual trust. Available plans and fees differ from state to state, and Medicaid age qualifications and income and eligibility rules are quite complicated. Therefore, it's best to consult with an elder care attorney before starting.

While everyone should write a will, not everyone needs a trust. Encourage the person you care for to prepare a will and to consider whether a trust would be helpful, too. If neither of these documents is created, your loved one's assets and belongings will be distributed according to state law after his or her death—and that may not be as he or she would wish.

Don't forget that as a caregiver, you need a will, too. In it, designate your beneficiaries and indicate your plans for handing over caregiving responsibilities in the event of your death.

Durable power of attorney

A durable power of attorney enables a person (the "principal") to appoint an agent, such as a trusted relative or friend, to handle specific legal and financial responsibilities. The document might confer the authority to pay bills or sell certain assets. Or it could extend to all financial decisions, including selling the family home, managing assets, and dealing with taxes.

A durable power of attorney is essential, because if a person becomes incapacitated or incompetent, without this document family and friends will not be allowed to make many important financial decisions or pay bills from the person's bank account. Nor can they do crucial Medicaid planning. Anyone who wishes to undertake these tasks would have to go to court and be officially appointed the person's guardian (see "Guardianship," page 28).

Some families rely on joint bank accounts as a way to give one person authority to manage another family

member's money. While this seems like an easy solution, it is not a good plan for many reasons. The additional person becomes a joint owner with the ability to use the property as their own, and the real owner may have little control over what a joint owner does. Debts of the joint owner could subject the property to legal action. Moreover, joint ownership over property matters that may require signatures of owners—such as transferring a house, care, or investments—will not be possible when one of the joint owners no longer has sufficient mental capacity to transact the business. For these reasons, a durable power of attorney is preferable.

It's enormously helpful to prepare this legal document long before the person starts having trouble handling financial and legal matters. At the time of the signing, the person establishing a durable power of attorney must be capable of deciding to seek assistance. Just like a trust, a durable power of attorney can be written so that the transfer of responsibilities occurs immediately or at a designated time, such as when a person becomes incapacitated. Until that point, the principal may choose to continue to retain these responsibilities.

People often balk at the thought of preparing and signing a durable power of attorney, because it looms as a big step closer to dependence. Another possible concern is that the agent they appoint will go against their wishes, which is why it's essential to choose someone who's trusted and to discuss the scope of his or her responsibility. You may wish to consider adding safeguards to the power of attorney, such as limiting the agent's authority to make gifts or requiring the agent to share all financial accounts and transactions with another person or persons on an annual basis, so that management is transparent.

The document can be revised or revoked at any time, as long as the person who signed it is considered competent. Otherwise, it stays in force until the principal dies. To learn more about the durable power of attorney, speak with a lawyer who has expertise in estate planning.

Advance directives

Most people value their ability and freedom to make choices, especially about the kind of medical treatment they receive. But if a person becomes incapacitated and is unable to make decisions about treatment or express those desires, advance directives (also called advance care directives) can help ensure that his or her wishes are still followed. These documents specify the person's preferences for health care and life-sustaining measures and name someone who will make health care decisions when the person is unable to do so.

Have your loved one create an advance directive while he or she is still able to. While you're at it, you may want to create one for yourself. Ideally, all adults should have a health care power of attorney, because you never know when a serious accident or injury could result in the loss of decision-making ability.

The following are four common types of advance directives. (Note that these documents go by different names in different states; see "Different terms, same concepts," page 27.)

A health care power of attorney is a document that a person uses to designate a health care agent (health care proxy) to act on his or her behalf, in the event that he or she becomes incapacitated and is unable to make decisions. The agent is usually a family member, but can also be a trusted friend. The person and his or her agent should have a thorough discussion about the person's values, priorities, and wishes beforehand, so that the agent will know what choices to make, should the need arise. This allows for flexibility under circumstances that can prove unpredictable. For example, mechanical ventilation (use of a machine to maintain breathing) may be desirable in an emergency if the person has a reasonable chance of recovery, but undesirable if ventilation will only prolong a painful dying process. Having a health care power of attorney also helps to avoid family fights over treatment decisions and can relieve your guilt if, for example, you carry out your loved one's wishes to refuse life support.

A living will sets forth medical wishes that will guide health care if a person becomes mentally or physically unable to make decisions. This is written when a person is healthy, but it needs to be reviewed periodically as the individual's situation changes. Note that while it is a legally binding document, it generally cannot require health care providers to follow medically inappropriate instructions. Moreover, the patient's current oral statements take precedence over the living will as long as he or she is able to make and communicate decisions. But if the person has lost that capacity, the living will holds sway to the extent that it provides useful guidance to a particular health decision, even if the person's beliefs on the matter have changed. Some experts believe that a legally binding living will limits choices in ways that are not in a person's best interest, because living wills are written before the individual knows all the facts and options surrounding a future health decision. Therefore, if he or she has a trusted person who can serve as health care agent, many experts recommend using that path instead.

A do-not-resuscitate (DNR) order tells health care personnel not to attempt cardiopulmonary resuscitation (CPR) if a person's heartbeat or breathing stops. Only a doctor can write a DNR, which can be one element of an advance directive. A DNR might be invoked if attempts to revive a person would not be successful or would lead to a level of physical or cognitive impairment that the person would find unacceptable, or if the person simply doesn't want heroic measures.

Physician orders for life-sustaining treatment (POLST) and its equivalent forms—MOLST, POST,

Different terms, same concepts

When it comes to advance directives, the terms used for them vary from state to state, just as laws do. Here are some synonyms for a few common terms.

Health care power of attorney: Also called a health care proxy form, medical power of attorney, durable power of attorney for health care, or appointment of a health care agent form.

Health care agent: Also called a health care proxy (or just proxy), surrogate, or representative, among other titles.

Living will: Also called a directive to physicians, health care declaration, or medical directive.

Do-not-resuscitate order (DNR): Also called a do-not-attempt-resuscitation order (DNAR) or allow-natural-death order (AND).

Physician orders for life-sustaining treatment (POLST): Also called physician orders for scope of treatment (POST), medical orders for life-sustaining treatment (MOLST), and medical orders for scope of treatment (MOST).

and MOST—are increasingly replacing DNRs because they are more comprehensive. They are written for people who are seriously ill right now or approaching the end of life. POLST translates the person's wishes into a physician-written medical order that is portable and effective across care settings—for example, from emergency treatment to a hospital or a nursing home. POLST addresses not only whether or not to attempt CPR, but also wishes regarding hospitalization and the intensity of treatment, from comfort care to full treatment. These forms are filled out with a physician and entered in the person's medical chart. Whatever form is used, make copies for both your care recipient and yourself. You or your loved one should carry a copy of the form at all times, and another copy should be posted in the person's home. (Many people tape them to the refrigerator, which is where emergency personnel know to look for them.) Other copies may be kept in the person's medical chart and your caregiver files.

Preparing advance directives

As you prepare such documents, it's wise to discuss all health care wishes and decisions with the doctor who is providing care for your loved one. Also, because state laws vary, it is important to make sure any advance directive complies with current laws in your state. A local hospital or seniors' organization may have staff members who can help you or your family member prepare an advance directive. Or a lawyer who is qualified in elder law or estate planning can assist you. An advance directive validly signed in one's home state will normally be effective in another state.

If you're selected as a health care agent, try to get as much information as possible about the person's preferences for medical treatment. Have a frank talk with a doctor about possible medical scenarios. If you're worried about how to broach the topic, consider the following suggestions.

Learn more about advance directives. Understanding these documents will help you handle your loved one's questions. One good source is Harvard Medical School's Special Health Report *Advance Care Planning: A guide to advance directives, living wills, and other strategies for communicating health care preferences.* (For ordering information, see "Resources," page 52.) Another good source is the Vermont Ethics Network (802-828-2909 or www.vtethicsnetwork.org). It offers information on end-of-life care and a questionnaire that prompts people to consider their medical values and how they feel about medical measures to prolong life. The Conversation Project (www.theconversationproject.org) is also an excellent resource to help you start the conversation.

Print out state-specific forms for your state. To download a copy of your state's advance directive, visit CaringInfo (www.caringinfo.org) and click on Advance Care Planning at the top of the page.

Find opportunities to talk with your loved one. Use a newspaper article or friend's experience to open a conversation about medical wishes. Or launch the conversation by mentioning that you are considering an advance care directive for yourself.

Ask a doctor to help. Medical professionals, especially those who deal with older or seriously ill patients, are often well versed in discussing these matters. Ask for help, or find out whether the doctor would be willing to raise the topic with your loved one.

Communicating your loved one's wishes

Once the proper documents have been prepared, it's important to clearly communicate the care recipient's wishes to the key people involved. As a caregiver, check that the following steps are taken:

- Provide all doctors who are caring for your loved one with a copy of the advance directive.
- Make sure anyone named as a health care agent has a copy of the document and knows the person's medical care choices.
- Explain the person's health care wishes to other family members. Be prepared to have a difficult conversation, because not everyone is comfortable discussing end-of-life care.
- Realize that you may need to have more than one discussion with doctors and family members. Revisit the advance directive annually, or whenever big changes occur in your loved one's health, to be sure the document still reflects his or her needs and goals.
- When the person is admitted to a hospital, ask the admitting or attending doctor to look at the directive and put it in the medical chart. You will likely have multiple doctors during a hospital stay. Don't assume they are all aware of the advance directive.

Guardianship

When no durable power of attorney or advance directives exist, and the person you are caring for is unable to make clear-headed decisions about health care, finances, or other aspects of life, a judicial guardianship or conservatorship may be the last resort (particularly if there is disagreement among family members about these issues). As usual, state terminology varies, but a majority of states use guardianship for the management of one's personal affairs and conservatorship for the management of financial affairs. In this discussion, guardianship will be used to refer to both.

Before considering a guardianship, other strategies to support the independence of the individual should be considered and tried. These include the use of support services to help with financial management or activities of daily living; technology to monitor the person's safety and routines; recruiting a cadre of informal supporters from family and neighbors; and in the case of family disputes over the best course of action, family mediation.

In order to act as someone's legal guardian, you have to go to court to have the person declared incompetent based on expert findings. However, incompetence is not an all-or-nothing matter, and courts today are encouraged to give the guardian only limited authority and to leave as much as possible in the hands of the disabled person. For example, one may need a guardian to manage one's living arrangements and finances but not health care decision-making. No two individuals have exactly the same needs.

If family members disagree about the need for guardianship or who should act as a guardian, this can be a painful, prolonged, and costly process that leaves everyone involved feeling angry, guilty, or both. Sadly, guardianship strips your loved one of many legal rights, including the ability to vote, marry, or make enforceable decisions about health care, finances, or living arrangements. Yet it may be the only way you can gain the legal authority to make decisions and carry out many essential tasks that he or she is no longer able to handle, such as paying bills or arranging admission to a nursing home.

State laws for gaining guardianship differ. Even if you bring the case to court, there is no assurance that you will be named guardian. In some cases, another family member may be appointed; in others, the role might go to an outside trustee, agency, or institution. As noted above, guardians can be given limited or broad authority, depending on what a court rules is needed after a thorough investigation. Sometimes the court doles out responsibilities to several parties. For example, a bank trustee might oversee financial decisions, while a family member handles more personal decisions, like living arrangements. Generally, the court requires reports and financial accounting at regular intervals, or whenever important decisions are made. ◗

Financial planning

M edical treatment and caregiving can be costly, which makes good financial planning essential. Get advice from an experienced financial planner, elder care attorney, geriatric care specialist, or social worker. Because financial assistance varies widely from state to state, it's best to seek advice from experts who live in the same area as the person receiving care, especially if you are arranging care from a distance.

Organizing finances

You might find yourself in charge of organizing your loved one's finances. If you do, start by compiling a list of his or her assets and liabilities (see "Steps to take," below). Then do some research or get professional advice to help you decide on the most appropriate financial options. Focus on the following.

Consider a durable power of attorney or a joint bank account. A durable power of attorney (see page 25) can give you the legal authority to pay bills from the person's bank account and oversee his or her finances. If no durable power of attorney exists, open-

Initially, caregiving may not include managing your loved one's finances. But as the illness progresses, you should be prepared to do so.

ing a joint bank account with the person you are caring for can make bill paying easier. If you choose a joint account, make sure only one signature is required, to avoid problems if the person becomes incapacitated.

Clean up the person's finances. Multiple bank accounts and retirement funds can be hard to track and manage. Create a list of existing accounts. Consolidate bank accounts, and consider doing the same with investment and money management accounts. Talk with a financial adviser about investment strategies.

Streamline deposits and payments. Online payments and automatic withdrawals ease the task of tracking and paying bills. A money manager, certified public accountant, or local bill-paying service can also handle this job for a fee; some will even come to the home. To prevent misplaced checks, set up automatic deposits for Social Security benefits and other income.

Trim expenses. Cost-saving measures can help ease financial burdens. Cancel unnecessary insurance policies, take advantage of discount drug options, and roll debt from several high-interest credit cards into one lower-rate card. Contact your local Agency on Aging to check on the availability of utility payment assistance, property tax relief for senior homeowners, and similar cost-saving programs.

Steps to take

G ood financial planning starts with gathering these materials:

- a list of income and assets (including real estate, bank accounts, items in safe deposit boxes, and investment or retirement accounts)
- a list of all recurring bills and liabilities
- all insurance policies.

Investigate the following:

- a joint bank account or durable power of attorney that allows you to pay bills
- insurance options (life, health, long-term care)
- a bill-paying system (such as automatic withdrawals, online bill payments, or a bill-paying company).

Share the cost. Consider asking family members to pay a portion of costs involved with care, or to pay you for your services.

Look for additional income. If your loved one is a homeowner, look into a reverse mortgage or establish a home equity line of credit to raise needed funds.

Managing money online

The days when you had to get in your car and drive to the bank are long past. Today, nearly half of consumers do all their banking online. Brokerage transactions and other financial dealings have also shifted into the virtual world. But while online financial dealings can streamline bill paying and investment management, they can also become problematic when a person becomes ill or infirm. Often, older adults keep haphazard records of their usernames and passwords.

It can be cumbersome—and possibly risky—to individually share each password and the answers to security questions for every financial website. One way to simplify this process is to set up a shared password manager. Products like 1Password (www.1password.com) and LastPass (www.lastpass.com) store all passwords in one secured digital location where approved family members and other designated individuals can get access.

The person who is receiving care should also keep—and share—a list of all the websites he or she uses to manage finances, including (where relevant)

- online banking institution(s)
- mortgage company
- credit card companies
- investment companies
- loan providers
- service providers (such as the gas and electric company, if bill payment isn't set up through a bank).

Finding benefits and services

Public benefits programs, such as Medicare, Medicaid, Social Security, and food stamps, have specific eligibility requirements. These requirements vary, but they usually involve a combination of age, income, assets, expenses, household size, health status, work history, and disability.

Acquaint yourself with programs that can pay directly for certain needs, such as prescription drugs (see "Medicare drug coverage," page 34) or home health aides. While these programs may cover only limited services, they can free up time and money, which you can then apply to other needs. Contact an experienced social worker or geriatric care manager for a comprehensive list of options.

Government benefits

The U.S. federal government offers a variety of benefits, including the following:

Social Security. Social Security payments are sent monthly to seniors who paid into the system while they were working, or to their beneficiaries (spouse, disabled children, and children who are below a certain age or attending school).

Supplemental Security Income (SSI). SSI is paid monthly to low-income seniors and blind or disabled people. SSI benefits may be reduced if the person you are caring for lives in your home; is not your spouse or child; and does not pay for food, shelter, and clothing. Benefits may be cut more severely or stopped if the person lives in a nursing home or hospital, unless the arrangement is only temporary.

Food stamps. This program—formally known as the Supplemental Nutrition Assistance Program, or SNAP—helps low-income people buy food, which may make healthy foods more affordable.

Veterans' benefits. These payments help cover the costs of care for people who were in the armed services. Benefits may include drugs, health care,

Did you know? | The National Family Caregiver Support Program requires states to publicize available services and help caregivers gain access to them. Support, training, respite care, and limited supplemental services may be offered, although available services vary greatly from state to state. In some cases, services may be limited. Check with your local Agency on Aging for details and eligibility requirements.

and nursing home care, although not every veteran is entitled to the broadest coverage. (For example, veterans with service-related disabilities get more extensive coverage.)

BenefitsCheckUp

This service from the National Council on Aging connects people 55 or older to hundreds of benefits that can help them pay for rent, property taxes, heating and utility bills, health care, prescription drugs, and other goods or services. The site offers a full benefits database, as well as a prescription drug coverage database. You can use these free services as often as you like.

The questionnaire at www.benefitscheckup.org takes less than half an hour to fill out. It requires personal financial information, but it is confidential. If the person appears to qualify for any programs, the service will provide contact information so you can request the benefit. You do need Internet access and computer skills to fill out the forms. If that poses an obstacle for you, you may be able to get help at a local library or senior center.

National, state, and local organizations

National organizations focused on a particular health condition—such as breast cancer, Alzheimer's disease, or Parkinson's disease—often can steer you toward specific sources of funds or assistance. Charitable foundations in your area may also offer assistance to people with certain health conditions.

In addition, many states sponsor programs that help fund health care. One example is Prescription Advantage in Massachusetts, which pays the portion of senior prescription drug costs not covered by other insurance. Another is the Program of All-Inclusive Care for the Elderly (PACE), which is offered in most states. This is a health care program for people who are frail enough to be eligible for nursing home care, but who still want to live independently at home. PACE offers a full range of health care services; adult day services with transportation, meals, social services, and occupational and physical therapy; prescription and nonprescription drugs; hospital or nursing home care; and respite care. If the person qualifies for Medicaid, then Medicare and Medicaid

together will cover the costs. Otherwise, you can pay for care with a combination of Medicare and private funds, such as long-term care insurance, personal savings, or investment income. Rarely, employer or state programs contribute a portion of the cost. Contact the National PACE Association (see "Resources," page 52) for more information.

Managing insurance policies

Insurance policies are often promoted as a safety net, but it's important to carefully assess what the policies actually offer and where there are holes in coverage. Policies are rarely easy to read, but it's in your best interest to check them carefully.

Health insurance. Medicare, Medicaid, and private health insurance may cover many caregiving costs. Insurance may partially or completely pay for medical equipment, adult day health services, nutritional supplements, acupuncture and other complementary care, massage, home health aides or homemaker services, respite care, health and home assessments, and many other products and services. Coverage offered through private health insurance and public health benefits varies widely. Read through the policy and call the insurer to check the specifics of coverage. Check with the Centers for Medicare and Medicaid Services (see "Resources," page 52) for information on government benefits.

Life insurance. Life insurance pays benefits upon a person's death. Some policies also act as collateral that the insured can borrow against. It may be possible to collect benefits early and apply them to home services or long-term care. Called "living benefits" or "accelerated benefits," these arrangements vary greatly in the amount paid out, how the funds are paid (as a lump sum or in regular payments), and who can invoke this option. Generally, the insured must have a year or less to live to take advantage of living benefits. Even when money is tight, it may not be a good idea to cash in life insurance. Often living benefits pay only a fraction of the policy's total value, and they may affect taxes and eligibility for other benefits, including Medicaid. Look closely at the costs and benefits of any offers before signing up for one of these programs. ♥

Navigating Medicare and Medicaid

Medicare offers health care for Americans ages 65 and older or those younger than 65 with a disability or end-stage renal disease, while Medicaid covers low-income people of any age. Following is some basic information about each program. For more detailed information, contact the Centers for Medicare and Medicaid Services, or see another Harvard publication called *Navigating Health Insurance*, which includes detailed information on these programs (see "Resources," page 52).

Medicaid

If the person you are caring for qualifies as low income, Medicaid will pay for certain medical and long-term care services, prescription drugs, and nursing home care.

Medicaid planning often requires forethought because you must have very few assets in order to qualify for coverage. In fact, many people have to "spend down" their assets until they reach a level required to qualify for long-term care, which could be as low as $2,000, excluding the value of a home and possibly a car. Be aware that eligibility requirements and rules about spending down vary by state. To receive the best and most up-to-date guidance, consult an elder care attorney with Medicaid experience.

Medicare

Medicare is split into Part A (hospital insurance), Part B (outpatient insurance), and Part D (prescription drug coverage). Parts A and B together are known as "traditional Medicare." Part C (also called Medicare Advantage) offers an alternative to traditional Medicare for people who prefer a managed care plan, along the lines of a health maintenance organization (HMO). Medicare Advantage plans are offered by Medicare-approved private insurance companies and are handled by managed care organizations. Here's a more detailed rundown of what the different parts cover:

Part A helps pay for hospital or short-term nursing home care, hospice services, doctor visits, lab tests while you are in the hospital, and some home health care. Although you don't have to pay a premium for Part A, there are some copayments and a yearly deductible.

Part B is optional and covers part of doctors' bills, outpatient care, home-based physical therapy, certain screenings and lab tests, and a limited number of prescription drugs (principally drugs administered in doctors' offices). There is a monthly premium and an annual deductible for Part B. Because there are still a lot of out-of-pocket expenses that aren't covered, most people on Medicare Parts A and B also buy a Medicare supplement plan, more commonly referred to as Medigap. Note that Medigap plans cannot be used to pay for out-of-pocket costs if you have a Medicare Advantage plan. If you have both, you need to either stop

---

Has your state opted for Medicaid expansion?

President Obama's Affordable Care Act (ACA) provided states with additional Medicaid funding to cover adults under age 65 whose income is up to 138% of the federal poverty level (for a single person, that's an income of up to $16,642 per year). Under a Supreme Court ruling, states are permitted to opt out of expanding Medicaid without having to pay a penalty. As of late 2018, 34 states, including Washington, D.C., have adopted Medicaid expansion, three states are discussing doing so, and 14 states have opted not to expand at this time. Some states have pursued program waivers, which give them more flexibility in designing their Medicaid program. Sometimes this helps consumers; sometimes it hurts them. To find out if your state participates in the Medicaid expansion program, contact the Centers for Medicare and Medicaid Services (www.cms.gov).

your Medicare Advantage plan and sign up for traditional Medicare or discontinue your Medigap plan.

Part C (Medicare Advantage) is made of up plans offered by private insurers. Medicare Advantage plans include all the services in Part A and Part B and usually Part D (prescription drug coverage). These plans may also include other benefits, such as vision, hearing, and dental programs. Typically, copayments and deductibles are lower than with standard Medicare, but the premium is higher. Because Medicare Advantage plans usually include prescriptions and sometimes other coverage, they can make paperwork easier. However, with many plans, the individual must see a doctor who is part of the plan's network or go to certain hospitals for care. About one-third of seniors have Medicare Advantage plans, while two-thirds opt for traditional Medicare.

Part D covers some prescription drug costs. Run by Medicare-approved private insurance companies, these plans typically have a monthly premium, a yearly deductible, and a copayment. Hundreds of these plans exist. For help deciding whether you need Part D or not, see "Medicare drug coverage," page 34.

Enrolling in Medicare or switching plans

There are certain time periods to be aware of when making any changes involving Medicare, based on whether you're enrolling in a plan for the first time or switching plans.

For those newly enrolling. There is a specific period during which people can enroll in Medicare for the first time. This period starts three months before an individual turns 65. It continues during the person's birth month and for three months afterward. It is important to sign up for Medicare during this initial enrollment period. If a person enrolls later, a penalty is added to that person's monthly Part B payment for as long as he or she receives Medicare Part B. The penalty can be as much as 10% of the Part B premium for each full 12-month period during which the individual was eligible but did not sign up. There may also be a penalty for late enrollment in Part D (see "Penalty," page 34).

Getting help

Plan comparisons, financial help, and other assistance are available through these sources:

- **Medicare** (www.medicare.gov) or toll-free at 800-MEDICARE (800-633-4227; TTY: 877-486-2048), for general information, a plan finder tool, prescription and generic drug lists, information on pharmaceutical assistance programs, financial aid information, and more

- **BenefitsCheckUp** (www.benefitscheckup.org) for national and local charitable aid to help with drug costs (and many more benefit programs)

- **Social Security Administration** (www.ssa.gov) or toll-free at 800-772-1213; TTY: 800-325-0778) for low-income aid called Extra Help

- **your state health insurance program** (call or check online at www.medicare.gov) for general information.

Although most people must sign up to receive Medicare, some people are automatically enrolled in Parts A and B. These include people who are already receiving Social Security benefits.

Consider getting Medigap within six months of enrolling in Medicare Part B. Insurance companies cannot deny coverage or request higher premiums because of existing health problems during that period; however, after that point, they can. For those who do not choose Medigap right away, there is an annual open enrollment period. Make sure the person you are caring for does not drop any current insurance to switch to a Medigap policy without first checking when open enrollment begins. Periods without coverage can be costly.

For those who want to switch plans. Unlike most health insurance, Medicare does not require enrollees to sign up each year. But that doesn't mean individuals are locked into their plans forever. It is not uncommon for people to move back and forth between traditional Medicare and Medicare Advantage—or switch from one Medicare Advantage or Part D plan to another—in order to cut costs or to receive certain benefit features. The time to do this is during the open enrollment period—October 15 to December 7. New plan coverage will start on January 1.

Medicare drug coverage

As noted, there are hundreds of these plans, run by Medicare-approved private companies. Plan options may be overwhelming or slim, depending on where the person receiving care lives. When you research plans, you will need the person's Medicare card and a list of all his or her prescription drugs. Typically, plans will not cover every drug (see "Read the fine print," page 35). Investigate options carefully. Check the plan's formulary—the list of drugs it covers—to make sure your loved one's medications are included. The costs of uncovered prescriptions can add up quickly. Often the formulary is available on the plan's website. Also check to see if the pharmacies in the plan are convenient for you and your loved one. If the Medicare recipient spends time in more than one place, choose a single permanent mailing address—usually the place where he or she resides for the majority of the year.

Even if the person you are caring for doesn't currently use medications or uses just a few, you'll probably want to investigate a prescription drug plan. Paying the premium can be a hedge against catastrophically high drug costs if a new illness, such as cancer, is diagnosed.

Tallying costs

Whether you are considering a prescription drug plan for the first time or wondering how your care recipient's existing plan compares to other available plans, you'll need to do some calculating. The various costs and limits on medications can make this a tricky equation. Here are some factors to consider as you weigh options. Be aware that plan costs can change yearly.

Premium. Monthly plan premiums can be paid directly to the company responsible for the drug plan or deducted from a Social Security check. Some plans don't charge any premium.

Deductible. Each calendar year, prescription coverage begins only after payments meet a deductible, which in 2018 could not exceed $405.

Coverage. Once the deductible is met, the participant is responsible for a copayment or coinsurance amount, which varies by plan. In some plans,

There are many Medicare drug plans, run by Medicare-approved private companies. It can take some work to compare the list of covered drugs from one plan to the next.

the copayment or coinsurance is always the same (for example, $10 per prescription or 25% of the drug's cost) and the plan pays the remainder. In other plans, common medications are placed in different tiers, each with different copayments. For example, the copayment might be $10 for drugs in Tier 1 and $60 for drugs in Tier 3.

Coverage gap. From the outset, Medicare drug plans had a gap in their coverage, sometimes referred to as the "donut hole." Once people entered that hole, they had to shoulder more of their drug costs themselves, which could add up. That hole began gradually shrinking after the Affordable Care Act (the ACA, or Obamacare) was passed in 2010. Prior to the ACA, Medicare stopped paying any share of prescription drug costs after the beneficiary had spent $2,830, and it started paying again only if and when the person's out-of-pocket expenses hit $4,550. During the gap, the person paid 100% of prescription drug costs. As of 2019, the donut hole no longer exists for brand-name prescription drugs, and enrollees will pay only their usual share of the cost of these drugs after meeting their deductible. The donut hole for generic drugs will close in 2020.

Catastrophic coverage. This starts automatically when someone has paid the out-of-pocket maximum ($5,000 in 2018). Then, through the end of the calendar year, the person is responsible only for a small coinsurance or copayment when buying covered drugs.

Penalty. Anyone who fails to enroll in Medicare

Part D once eligible and chooses to enroll later may incur a monthly penalty equal to 1% of the "national base beneficiary premium" ($35.02 in 2018). The penalty doesn't apply to anyone who currently has drug coverage through other benefits, but it is initiated if a person loses those benefits and fails to apply for Medicare Part D promptly. The penalty may also be waived for people of low income.

Protecting your loved one's interests

Medicare Part D has had its share of surprises and glitches. Following these tips may help you avoid pitfalls and resolve any problems that crop up.

Read the fine print. Sometimes hurdles exist, even for covered drugs. A plan may request a statement from a doctor for certain covered drugs, or it may require the person to try a generic drug before it will pay for a brand-name drug. Sometimes plans drop drugs from their formulary. That's why it's best to double-check that the drugs your loved one needs are covered by making a phone call before enrolling, even if you've already done an online search. Make sure any quantity limits on particular drugs fit your loved one's needs.

Cut costs. People on Medicare who have sufficiently low income can qualify for assistance with premiums and prescription drug copayments through the Medicare Low-Income Subsidy (call Social Security toll-free at 800-772-1213 to learn more). You can also cut costs by choosing generics or less costly prescription drugs, and by purchasing drugs through mail-order discount pharmacies. The Medicare website (www.medicare.gov) offers lists of state and national pharmaceutical assistance programs.

Keep records. Keep an annual file with copies of your family member's Medicare and health care plan cards and explanation of benefits. Save receipts for covered drugs, so you can request reimbursement and have a record of payments made. Plans automatically record this information when the subscriber buys covered drugs within their networks, but they usually require receipts for medications bought elsewhere. ♥

Medical planning

Advance directives are vital legal and medical documents that should be filled out as soon as possible, while your loved one is still able to make the decisions these documents entail. But advance directives will only guide decisions concerning life-sustaining measures and end-of-life care. Good medical planning throughout the course of your loved one's illness or disability is another matter—and is much more involved. As a caregiver, it's likely that you'll need to work closely with your family member's primary care physician or specialist. If you're caring for an older adult, you may also find it helpful to work with a geriatrician, a physician who specializes in caring for older adults.

Choosing doctors

One cornerstone of good medical care is having an experienced, approachable primary care doctor who can coordinate care and help a patient connect with specialists as needed. If your loved one doesn't have a primary care doctor or if the current doctor isn't a good fit, you may need to help find a new one. The following tips may be useful.

Geriatricians have experience dealing with the complex medical conditions of older patients. Another plus is that they recognize the importance of allowing family members to attend appointments.

Check with insurance providers first. While Medicare and Medicaid policies usually offer people free rein to choose doctors, some doctors won't take many, or any, new Medicare or Medicaid patients. On the other hand, many HMOs and other types of insurance restrict patients to certain preferred providers.

Ask around. Recommendations from friends, neighbors, and co-workers can give you important insights. Is the doctor easy to talk to? Does he or she return phone calls swiftly? How quickly can you get an appointment? Consider how available and open to questions a doctor will be. You can also find detailed doctor reviews on websites like Healthgrades (www.healthgrades.com) and Vitals (www.vitals.com). Any primary care doctor you choose should be board-certified in family or internal medicine, or in geriatrics.

Schedule an initial meeting. Once you gather a few names, see if any of the doctors would be willing to have a preliminary meeting. Preferably both you and your loved one should attend. (Some physicians will do meet-the-doctor visits, while others won't. Note that Medicare will pay for the visit only if the patient is there.) Ask plenty of questions: Does the doctor often see patients of this age or with these ailments? Is he or she comfortable working with other family members? How would he or she approach any disagreements over medical issues? At which hospitals does the doctor have admitting privileges? If your loved one is in a hospital or nursing home, will the doctor visit him or her there and help coordinate care?

Consider the location. A primary care doctor should be able to provide local referrals, but sometimes the best care isn't available nearby. Research the options. Decide whether the promise of cutting-edge treatment is worth the travel required and, possibly, being separated from supportive family and friends at a difficult time. A local medical team may also be able to arrange for an experimental treatment.

Ask about access to health information. The 2003 privacy law amendments to the Health Insurance Portability and Accountability Act (HIPAA) have repercussions for caregivers (see "Taking part in health care visits," below). Doctors and other health professionals are required by law to have written permission to share health and medical billing information with a third party. Although some providers will share information if you identify yourself as a caregiver, others will not. You may need a health care proxy form or a signed waiver permitting information to be shared. There is no single form for this. Providers should have their own form for you to sign. More information is available at www.hhs.gov/ocr/hipaa or by calling the U.S. Department of Health and Human Services toll-free at 866-627-7748.

Why choose a geriatrician?

It's not unusual for someone to see the same doctor for decades. But as a person grows older, it's wise to consider switching to, or at least consulting with, a geriatrician. Geriatricians have expertise in dealing with the medical complexities of older patients who have many chronic conditions. They are trained to consider the needs of the whole person and focus on function and quality of life. Some geriatricians routinely make home visits to see how a patient lives and what modifications could improve safety, nutrition, function, and mobility. They recognize the importance of allowing family members to attend appointments and can coordinate care with specialists.

Geriatricians are also well aware of harmful effects that medications can have on older people. People over 65 often have numerous health problems, for which they are prescribed multiple medications. The more medications a person takes, the higher his or her risk of drug interactions and adverse side effects. The elderly are especially vulnerable to side effects because their bodies process drugs differently than younger people's do. Even over-the-counter medications or supplements can be problematic, and the effects can be cumulative.

About one in 10 hospital admissions in older adults is due to an adverse drug reaction, but up to half of these events are preventable. That's why it's essential to keep tabs on possible drug interactions and to calibrate pain medications carefully. Unfortunately, doctors who are not experienced in caring for older patients may dismiss signs of adverse drug reactions as dementia or depression. A geriatrician has the specialized expertise to evaluate an individual's medi-

Taking part in health care visits

The Health Insurance Portability and Accountability Act (HIPAA) shields sensitive health information from prying eyes. HIPAA is instrumental in protecting your privacy, but it can also limit access to information that caregivers need.

When it comes to participating in doctor visits, sometimes the patient is the one blocking access out of a desire for continued independence or for fear of an overly intrusive caregiver. Either way, some caregivers can find themselves shut out of visits and denied a voice in the person's care. This is problematic, considering that the caregiver has the greatest insight into a patient's day-to-day care, overall health, symptoms, medication adherence, and any side effects from medications. Having the caregiver in the room during appointments—and allowing him or her access to the person's medical files—can ensure the doctor has enough information to make the most educated treatment decisions.

One way for caregivers to circumvent this problem and gain access to medical information is to be named as the recipient's health care agent via a health care power of attorney. Otherwise, it's up to the patient and doctor to decide how much access the caregiver is allowed.

Have a conversation with your loved one about being in the room during doctor visits and having access to his or her medical information. Let the person know why it's so important for you to be a part of this process.

Also discuss your caregiving needs with the doctor. The ability to communicate directly with the doctor is especially important if you're caring for someone with dementia, because the person may not be able to clearly explain any problems or understand the current treatment plan. If you're a long-distance caregiver and you can't attend medical appointments in person, ask to listen in on the phone during these visits.

cations and recommend changing or stopping certain drugs to avoid potential problems.

A geriatrician can also use a variety of means to improve a person's quality of life and ability to live independently, such as writing a referral to a physical therapist or occupational therapist, offering recommendations on home adaptations for safety and accessibility, or giving advice on home care services. Geriatricians have extensive contacts with community-based service providers, thereby easing the burden on the caregiver. In addition, they are trained to understand the caregiver's role and its accompanying challenges.

Medicare or Medicaid will pay for a comprehensive geriatric evaluation. Some private insurance plans also provide coverage if the primary care physician makes a referral. The geriatrician can serve in a consultative role or as the primary care physician.

Selecting a hospital

In a medical emergency, such as a stroke or heart attack, you will probably not have a choice of hospital. The ambulance will take you to the closest facility— and since time is of the essence in a life-threatening situation, this generally represents the best choice. (If the condition is not life-threatening and if the EMT feels there is enough time, it's preferable to go to the hospital where your doctor works, since your medical records will be there.)

After the initial crisis is resolved, should you consider a move to a "better" hospital? If the care is attentive and effective and the medical team is responsive and communicates well, stay put. A more prestigious hospital does not automatically ensure better care. However, if your loved one needs specialized care that's not available at your local hospital, a transfer will be necessary.

If you are concerned about the quality of care your loved one is receiving, your best bet is to first talk to the physician. Treat a move to another hospital as a last resort. If the hospital's staff isn't effectively communicating or addressing the person's needs, press hard for answers and more responsive care. Get the patient's primary care doctor involved. Call upon the hospital's patient advocate for assistance, and request a second medical opinion, if necessary.

Preparing for a hospital stay

A hospital stay introduces a whole new set of issues. Here are a few tips to help your loved one get through a hospital stay and to ease the transition back home.

Be prepared. Caregivers should always keep an updated list of medications handy in case of an unexpected hospitalization. Other useful items include contact information for primary care providers and specialists, insurance card numbers and financial information, and copies or originals of any advance directives. When the hospitalization is for a planned procedure, both the patient and caregiver will have a chance to prepare for the hospital stay and the return home. Learn which home modifications you'll need to make for the person's safety and comfort, and consider how he or she will handle stairs and daily tasks such as dressing, bathing, eating, or cooking. Ask the doctor whether it's worth investing in any assistive devices or paid help to make life easier when the person comes home. Investigate rehabilitation options, particularly after hip replacement or knee surgery. Visit several rehabilitation centers to make an informed choice.

Get connected. Ask a few questions right away. While the patient is in the hospital, who can you contact for health updates and other concerns regarding the person's stay? Should you speak to the nurse, or will a case manager be assigned? What is the best

---

A CAREGIVER'S PERSPECTIVE

"My mother was completely disoriented about time and where she was. She couldn't really remember anything from one conversation to the next. After about a year and a half, she started seeing a geriatrician. This doctor looked at her chart and said, 'What is this woman doing on Valium? Side effects of Valium mimic dementia.'"

— *Beth, 41, who helps care for her 79-year-old mother*

number and time to call? When should you expect to know the plan for each day? When does the attending physician make rounds?

Be an extra set of eyes and hands. Alert the health care providers to any worrisome behavior or symptoms your loved one may have, such as hallucinations, difficulty breathing, confusion, or depression. Ask about any medications your loved one receives to make sure they are the correct ones, as prescribed. Provide glasses and hearing aids, along with comforts of home such as warm nonslip socks and slippers, a bathrobe, and moisturizers for skin and lips. As soon as it is safe for the person to sit up in a chair and walk, help with these activities when staff members are busy—but first, learn how to do so safely. Visit at mealtimes, when you can, to assist with eating and make it a more social occasion.

Jot down medical questions and answers. Keep a written list to help you stay organized and get all the answers you need once you have the ear of a busy doctor or nurse. Write down any responses so you can refer back to them later.

Look toward the future. Consider what will happen after the hospital care is complete. Will the patient go home or to a rehabilitation center? How long will rehabilitation take? How will the person feel after discharge, and will he or she be able to get around independently? Will home health care or home modifications be necessary? Are disabilities likely to be temporary or permanent? Discuss these issues with a case manager or social worker, as well as with the doctors and nurses.

Get clear discharge instructions. Ask plenty of questions. Find out whom to call if problems arise during a transfer to another facility or once the patient is home. Which warning signs should you watch for? When should the person take medication and for how long? What are the possible side effects of any drugs prescribed? What steps can you take to help speed the person's recovery? What activities are permitted and which should be avoided or added slowly? How will future tests or follow-up appointments be scheduled? Make certain that plans are in place to get assistance or make home modifications, if necessary.

Make a follow-up appointment. Before leaving the hospital or rehabilitation center, contact the primary care doctor to schedule an appointment within a week after discharge. Bring discharge instructions to the appointment. ♥

When your loved one needs more care

Sometimes you can meet changing needs by stepping up services and assistance from paid or informal caregivers, or by moving your loved one closer to family. Other times it's necessary to consider options for long-term care. The best time to plan for this care is well before it is needed.

Planning ahead permits you to thoroughly research options and allows time to move up the lengthy waiting list that many good facilities have. Try to get on the waiting lists of up to three different places. That way, if a spot opens up at one facility before your loved one is ready, you'll have at least one other waitlist as a backup. (You're under no obligation to take an open spot that's offered.) And, in the case of nursing homes, applying while money is less of an issue may open more doors than if you are relying on Medicaid alone. Nursing homes get a higher reimbursement rate from private-pay clients and are often eager to have them. Finally, planning ahead allows you to arrange the person's finances.

Finding qualified home care—or a good nursing home—requires research. Ask social workers, doctors, nurses, friends, family members, co-workers, and acquaintances for their advice. Whenever possible, visit any place you are considering or interview home nursing candidates.

In-home care

Often the first step up from covering your loved one's needs by yourself is to get help from friends and relatives. Or, you can hire someone to assist with activities of daily living, such as cooking, shopping, bathing, dressing, and giving medication, although you will generally have to pay out of pocket for these services. The following types of caregivers and services can help with these tasks.

Certified nursing assistants. These nurses' aides typically have taken a training course in basic nursing skills. They are not nurses and are not allowed to administer medications if they're sent by an agency, but they can help with activities such as bathing, dressing, and personal care.

Hired companions and homemakers. These assistants can help with meals, shopping, and laundry; supervise activities; and provide companionship and sometimes transportation. Some hired companions may also be willing to help with personal care. You may be able to set up a money-saving arrangement—such as allowing a college student to live in the home rent-free in exchange for help.

Home health aides. Home health aides perform personal services, such as bathing and dressing, and they may do light housekeeping.

Meal programs. Hot, nutritious meals are available through organizations like Meals on Wheels America (www.mealsonwheelsamerica.org) or Eating Together (www.eatingtogether.com). The latter offers lunch and companionship at community centers, sometimes with transportation (check with your

When your loved one needs more care than you can provide, there are many options to consider, including home health aides, certified nursing assistants, and adult day care.

state's Department of Aging to see if this service is available in your area). Senior centers, community groups, or religious organizations may have similar types of services.

Case managers. Health insurance plans or primary care clinics may assign case managers to oversee and coordinate health care. Often, case managers are registered nurses or social workers. They help coordinate services, keep tabs on a patient's progress, and communicate with the patient, along with his or her caregiver, family, doctors, and medical office billing departments.

Nurses. Nurses offer skilled nursing care, such as inserting intravenous lines, cleaning wounds, and changing bandages. They can also administer medications.

Physical, occupational, or speech therapists. Physical therapists use exercises and other methods to help the care recipient maintain strength and flexibility. Occupational therapists teach techniques to help with everyday activities requiring manual dexterity. Speech therapists can help with communication, as well as with swallowing issues. These trained professionals may do in-home therapy sessions.

Respite care workers. Respite care workers provide temporary care to give the caregiver some welcome time off.

Transportation services. Some communities offer free or low-cost transportation to medical appointments for seniors or people who are disabled. Other good sources of free or low-cost assistance are religious and community organizations such as churches or synagogues, Agencies on Aging, and senior centers.

In addition, United Way (www.unitedway.org) and other national organizations may be able to provide you with referrals to services in your community, along with helpful information and assistance. For example, the Alzheimer's Association offers a 24-hour help line (800-272-3900) and support groups throughout the country. Some of its chapters also offer training programs, assistance with care coordination, and other services.

Another good resource is the National Health Information Center (www.health.gov/nhic), which can help you locate resources in your area. A local Agency on Aging, geriatric care manager, hospital case manager, or social worker can also advise you about local services and may be able to suggest ways to cover the costs.

Adult day care

There may come a time when you need more help than in-home care providers can offer. This is where day care can be a great asset. An adult day care center can provide the person you're caring for with physical activities and social opportunities, while giving you a much-needed break or time to go to work.

Day care services may include transportation, nursing care, meals, personal care (such as help with bathing or toilet use), and rehabilitation therapy. Such facilities are immensely helpful if your loved one needs supervision or assistance with daily activities, health care, or social support for physical or cognitive impairments. Typically, adult day services are open during normal business hours. Some also offer evening and weekend hours. Day care services are not covered by Medicare, so plan to pay for them out of pocket.

Rehabilitation care

Whether it follows a sudden stroke or heart attack, a hip fracture, or even long-planned surgery, your loved one may need rehabilitation before coming home after a hospital stay. If he or she needs this type of transitional care, visit any rehabilitation centers you are considering. Ask friends and co-workers for recommendations. Your loved one's case manager should be able to help you set up a visit. Take a careful look at the environment: Is the facility clean and comfortable? Does the staff seem friendly and helpful? Bring along a list of questions. Here are some to get you started:

- What services are available? What will be provided?
- Who will be part of the care team—a physical therapist, speech therapist, case manager, nurse practitioner, physician?
- What percentage of patients are sent home after receiving care? How many go to a nursing home or long-term care facility afterward?

- What percentage of patients are readmitted to a hospital within 15 days of being discharged from your program?
- What are your staff qualifications? Is the facility accredited by a major accrediting body, such as the Joint Commission (formerly the Joint Commission on Accreditation of Healthcare Organizations) or the Commission on Accreditation of Rehabilitation Facilities?
- What is the average length of stay for people with the same condition as this patient?
- How many hours of therapy will the person have each day?
- How is progress measured?
- How often are meetings scheduled to discuss the patient's care?
- How often does a physician check in with patients? Can the patient's primary care physician visit?
- What is the patient-to-staff ratio?
- Will the patient be in a private or shared room?
- Will the patient receive rehabilitation treatment individually or in a group?

Making a move

Moving someone you love to an assisted living facility or a nursing home is fraught with painful feelings for all involved. Yet turning your loved one's safety and medical care over to trained professionals can be a great relief. And if a move enables you to spend more quality time with your loved one and expands his or her social opportunities, it may prove to be a blessing. Rather than focusing only on the guilt and sadness you feel, put some energy toward imagining how you might ease this passage.

Consider whether you can

- find ways to make this new place more comfortable and homey
- call at prearranged times to chat
- stop by for brief visits, such as during meals
- listen to music together if conversation is hard to sustain
- send emails, letters, or the occasional book
- make connections with staff and other residents
- plan regular outings to a movie or restaurant, a drive to a well-loved place, or time with family and friends.

- What items—such as toiletries, hearing aids, clothing, and a small amount of money—should your loved one bring to the facility? Are personal items such as photographs allowed?
- When are meals scheduled?
- When are visiting hours?
- How can family members get involved? Are family conferences offered to keep relatives informed of the patient's progress?

You can also use these questions as a foundation for evaluating long-term facilities.

Long-term care

Although most people first think of a nursing home when they consider long-term care, it isn't the only way to provide your loved one with support and give you some of your life back. Depending on the individual's needs and budget, you may wish to also consider the following possibilities.

- Senior apartments and subsidized senior housing enable residents to live independently, but many offer assistance with tasks such as shopping and laundry. Buildings are designed for maximum accessibility.
- Continuing care retirement communities (CCRCs) offer a series of step-up service options. Residents generally start in independent apartments, but with one to three meals per day, common areas, activities, an on-site medical clinic, and a bit of extra assistance, such as light housekeeping once a week. Over time, they can graduate into increasing levels of care, such as assistance with bathing, dressing, and taking medications. Some communities include a nursing home for residents to eventually move into.
- Group homes, sometimes called board and care homes, offer help with activities of daily living for those not in need of nursing home services. Often, these homes are not carefully monitored, however, and Medicare or Medicaid funds do not always pay for them.
- Assisted living facilities have private apartments, plus varying amounts of assistance with daily tasks and nursing supervision. Although these are

At some point, it may be necessary to move your loved one into a residential facility of some sort, where greater assistance is available. Places to consider include assisted living facilities and continuing care retirement communities.

often part of CCRCs, they can also be independent facilities.

• Skilled nursing facilities (nursing homes) offer long-term, around-the-clock care for people with significant illnesses or mental or physical disabilities. Some have units that specialize in caring for people with Alzheimer's disease and other forms of dementia.

A local Agency on Aging, geriatric care manager, or social worker should be able to help you find options in your area. Online tools from the Centers for Medicare and Medicaid Services can help you assess nursing homes and home health care agencies on its approved list (see "Resources," page 52).

For issues or complaints connected to nursing homes, contact the National Citizens' Coalition at 202-332-2275. You can also find a list of state or local long-term care ombudsmen at www.ltcombudsman.org or by calling the Eldercare Locator at 800-677-1116.

Hospice care

Hospice programs offer comfort and support for those reaching the end of life. Generally, Medicare and other insurers will cover the costs of hospice care if a patient is expected to live six months or less and chooses hospice rather than curative care.

Generally the process starts when the doc-tor writes an order admitting the person to hospice care. That care can then be provided at home, in a nursing home, or at a hospice facility or hospital. Hospice team members typically include a doctor, nurse, hospice aide, social worker, spiritual adviser, and volunteers. Their goal is to provide any medications, equipment, or services needed to keep the person comfortable, without providing curative therapies for the condition. A doctor will oversee the individual's care, which will be administered by the rest of the hospice team. The nurse will perform tasks such as administering pain medicine, dressing skin sores, monitoring vital signs, and helping with breathing or swallowing.

An aide may help with everyday tasks like bathing and eating. A spiritual adviser can provide emotional support and prayer.

Hospice services have been available for decades, so many Americans have some sense of the core idea that hospice involves a shift away from treating disease and prolonging life, and toward ensuring comfort. Still, hospice administrators, doctors, and nurses say many Americans have misconceptions about hospice.

Below are a few of the important things you should know about hospice care.

Hospice is primarily a service, not a place. The majority of Americans who enter hospice receive care in the home. A much smaller percentage get their care in hospitals, dedicated hospice facilities, or long-term care facilities.

Hospice doesn't mean full-time nursing. In emergencies (for example, if the caregiver gets sick, or the patient's pain suddenly increases), some agencies offer four-hour allotments of so-called continuous care. But for the most part, hospice services in this country don't mean full-time nursing. So if the person has difficulty bathing or going to the bathroom on his or her own, many families pay out-of-pocket for additional nursing or home health aide assistance. And if the person is in a nursing home, Medicare doesn't cover the room and board charges. Patients must have insurance that covers these costs, or else families will have to pay for them.

Offering access to services is not the same as providing them. Medicare-certified hospice providers must offer patients the services of registered nurses, home health aides, hospice physicians, and chaplains. But aside from the requirement that a nurse visit once every two weeks, Medicare doesn't regulate how often those services are actually provided. In most cases, this works out fine. Every person is different, and giving hospice agencies some flexibility makes sense. On the other hand, patients and their loved ones should be aware that a hospice agency has a lot of latitude in determining what services it provides, and families should ask (and push, if necessary) for additional services they believe are needed.

Every patient is required to have a care plan. One way to keep tabs on the services provided is to ask for a copy of the care plan, which Medicare requires each patient to have. The plan should spell out, for example, how often a home health aide will visit. Medicare also requires that hospice agencies keep records showing that the care plan has been followed. The plans should be reviewed every two weeks and adjusted as the person's condition changes. Families can ask for a copy of the care plan.

Patients don't have to give up their doctors. Sometimes people are hesitant about hospice because they think they can't keep their doctors. Similarly, doctors may fear that they are going to lose control over their patients' care. But Medicare encourages doctors to "follow" patients into hospice, with hospice medical directors remaining in the background as consultants.

Hospice doesn't mean the end of medical care, even if it prolongs life. Under Medicare, patients in hospice agree not to get curative treatments for a terminal condition. But treatment may continue if it's keeping the person comfortable, or it's treating conditions that are unrelated to the terminal illness. Hospice patients sometimes receive life-prolonging treatment for its own sake, unrelated to pain or other physical symptoms, if the extra time would serve some spiritual or emotional need—for example, giving a loved one time to visit.

Care related to the admitting illness is the responsibility of the hospice provider. Doctors and patients often think that choosing hospice means opting out of conventional Medicare coverage entirely, but that's not the case. The hospice provider must cover the costs of any care related to the patient's terminal illness—known as the "admitting illness." But for conditions not related to the admitting illness, regular Medicare coverage kicks back in.

Volunteers are vital. Many community hospices have large groups of volunteers who can give families an occasional break from caregiving duty so they can run an errand, take a nap, or attend to a child. One advantage some nonprofit hospice programs have over their for-profit counterparts is their volunteers.

Bereavement counseling is supposed to be available. Hospice services shouldn't end when the patient dies. Medicare requires agencies to provide bereavement services to families for up to a year after the death. Bereavement itself can have debilitating consequences. There's little oversight of the bereavement requirement, so hospice agencies may not always provide the services they should.

Additional information is available toll-free from Hospicelink at 800-331-1620, and from the National Hospice and Palliative Care Organization at 800-646-6460 or www.nhpco.org. ◆

Care for the caregiver

If you're fortunate, many of the tasks you undertake for your loved one will feel deeply satisfying to you. Perhaps caregiving offers a way for you to return the love and attention you received from a parent in the past, or to pay it forward to someone else who is important to you, or to uphold the value system by which you try to live. Even though you're bound to experience strain and difficult days, having a sense of purpose may help lighten your load.

Not everyone feels this way, of course. Nor is it possible to remain focused on a higher purpose every moment of the day. Sometimes the burden is too heavy to bear, even when you love the person you are helping. Some situations are especially hard—dementia or terminal illness in a loved one, for example, or the job of caring for a relative who is difficult or has been abusive (see "Caring for someone difficult," page 10).

It's important to acknowledge that caregiving is a tough, lonely job at times. Providing constant care is especially demanding, and roughly 10% of caregivers feel their health has suffered as a result of their responsibilities, according to the Family Caregiver Alliance. Caregivers are more likely than those who don't care for someone to experience physical complaints like headaches and pain. And when they become ill, they often neglect to go to the doctor, fill prescriptions, or take care of themselves in other ways.

As a caregiver, you frequently act with someone else's health in mind. Why not give the same consideration to your own health? The better you feel, the easier it will be for you to offer the best quality of help to the person in your care.

Gaining support

Support may come in many forms. Lean on a combination of caring family, friends, and neighbors, plus professional or government services.

Find assistance. Try your local Agency on Aging or Benefits-CheckUp to see what options are available for respite care and other services. Organizations like the American Cancer Society or Multiple Sclerosis Foundation may be able to link you with low-cost or free programs and services. AARP and government publications can help you locate caregiver services and choose among long-term care options. A consultation with a geriatric care manager or social worker may help you identify services in your area.

Caregiving offers you a way to return the love of a parent. But it's also important to acknowledge that caregiving is a tough, lonely job at times.

© FredFroese | Getty Images

Help for children who serve as caregivers

Currently, about 1.4 million children between the ages of 8 and 18 across the United States serve as caregivers to an adult in their household. These children assist with medications, prepare meals, move their loved ones in and out of bed, and help with personal tasks such as dressing, bathing, and using the toilet.

An advocacy and support organization called the American Association of Caregiving Youth (AACY) has been created to address the issues surrounding this "hidden population." Its mission is to provide respite relief, help with anxiety and depression, increase children's satisfaction level, and help these youngest caregivers balance responsibilities at home with their schoolwork. For more information on this program, visit www.aacy.org.

Investigate informal assistance. Can any friends and neighbors stop by to lend a hand? Does a local religious organization offer visits or emotional support? Many people may be willing to help, or to call you if anything seems amiss with your loved one.

Ask for help. Tell friends and family the job is too much for you to handle alone. Ask them to help brainstorm solutions. Accept help when it's offered. Some people will make specific offers of help. Encourage others to choose from a list of needed tasks, or assign jobs you've matched to their capabilities. Those who seem reluctant to do hands-on tasks may be able to help by covering costs, tracking down available government assistance, or taking over bill paying. Sometimes getting a few promises in place—to handle transportation to medical appointments or dinners on specific days—makes a big difference. Remember to thank everyone. A little pat on the back can help keep someone on the job.

Be honest with the person receiving care. It's not easy to have multiple people coming in and out of the home to provide care, but explain that your own health and well-being rely upon the division of labor. Be sensitive to the person's feelings—about being a burden, about spending money, about having a stranger help with personal tasks—but press your case firmly. One way to do so might be to say: "I wish I could continue doing _____, but I just can't. You're very important to me and it would be a great relief if I knew that your needs and my needs were both being met."

Get emotional support, too. Emotional support can come from many places, including a sympathetic partner or spouse, and friends who are willing to listen. Try to choose people who aren't judgmental. Ask outright if you can use them as a sounding board whenever the need arises. If only one person in your circle is willing to offer support, try not to over-burden him or her. Consider other sources of support as well.

Try a support group. Many organizations, hospitals, health care plans, and religious organizations offer support groups for caregivers. A doctor, nurse, or social worker may be able to steer you toward one of these groups. Support groups are a good place to blow off steam and share ideas with people who are facing similar situations. Some support groups meet online, which can be easier for homebound caregivers. Hotlines can help as well, especially when a crisis strikes suddenly. If you're not comfortable sharing your personal story with a group, a geriatric care manager may be able to provide you with support and perspective.

Consider therapy. If you find caregiving to be emotionally stressful, talk to a therapist. Up to 38% of caregivers say it's very stressful (see Figure 1, page 47). Depression is also common—between 40% and 70% of caregivers have significant symptoms of depression, with one-quarter to one-half of them meeting the definition of major depression. If you frequently feel depressed or overwhelmed, get help from a psychiatrist or therapist. Check your insurance company's list of providers in your area, or ask your doctor for a referral.

Involving family members

When a sudden medical emergency occurs—say, a spouse has a stroke or a parent is diagnosed with cancer—family members often join together for a common purpose, at least for a while. This type of collaboration is less likely when an aging parent is in slow decline. When few or no adult children live nearby, day-to-day problems are more likely to go unnoticed and unsolved. If you feel burdened by the caregiving responsibilities in your family and frustrated by the lack of assistance, the following suggestions may help ease your situation.

Call a family meeting. Hold a family meeting in person or by phone. Decide what kind of care is needed and who should research or provide it. Having a doctor, social worker, or geriatric care manager present can help enormously. The needs questionnaire in this report or a professional assessment can guide you, too. Try to put aside personal differences and resentments so that the spotlight stays on your loved one's needs. While it's helpful to have one person assume primary responsibility for caregiving, everyone in the family should offer to handle specific tasks.

Appoint a medical coordinator. Put one person in charge of talking with doctors, nurses, and pharmacists. That person should create a medical file that includes information on the patient's current illnesses, medications, allergies, medical history, specialists, and treatments. Keep a log that includes notes from conversations with doctors, insurance provid-

ers, hired caregivers, and others, including action steps and follow-up plans. It helps if the person who is appointed has some knowledge of health care, but more important is the ability to gather information, keep everyone in the family up to date, and push for responsive care. Sometimes it works well to have a second person who agrees to be a strong, vocal (and perhaps less polite) advocate should the need for one arise.

Play to strengths. Match people's tasks to their abilities. Those with medical backgrounds, financial abilities, or legal knowledge should put these skills to use. Practically anyone can make necessary phone calls to dig up information or oversee various aspects of caregiving.

Delegate. Create a list of smaller jobs that people can do, and distribute these tasks. Or simply ask people to check off what they can do. Keep a family email or phone list to help delegate tasks.

Recognize everyone's abilities (and limitations). Some people just can't pitch in or may have valid reasons to avoid doing so. Other pressing obligations, personal issues such as alcoholism, sadness over the circumstances, trouble coping, and even divided loyalties—such as those that crop up in stepfamilies—can all influence a person's willingness and availability to help.

Plan a trial period. Once family members agree on a plan, set a time to reassess it. If the situation is relatively stable, have a reassessment in one or more months. If the situation is uncertain, check in daily or weekly.

Be supportive. If you're not the main caregiver, ask how you can help. Could you take over for a weekend or one evening a week? Can you perform or coordinate certain services, such as housecleaning, yard work, or transportation to medical appointments? Can you pay for help or respite care?

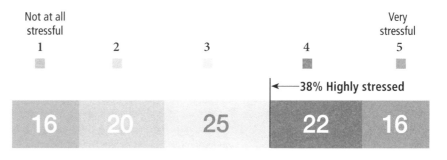

Figure 1: The emotional stress of caregiving

Almost four in 10 caregivers (38%) consider their caregiving duties to be very stressful emotionally. However, 16% say their responsibilities aren't stressful at all.

Source: National Alliance for Caregiving, Caregiving in the U.S. 2015.

Don't make promises you cannot keep, but do offer to help as much as possible. If you live in another state, make yourself available on specific weekends or during vacations. Keep in regular contact with the caregiver and the person receiving care.

Seeking balance

When you're a caregiver, your time is often divided and rarely your own. A minor medical emergency can make it impossible for you to get to work or to focus once you get there. You can become so overbooked with caregiving tasks that you don't have time to attend to others who need you, too. It can become impossible to socialize with friends because you don't have anyone to stay with the person you're caring for. Seeking balance doesn't automatically ensure that these situations will change. But redistributing some of the burden can make your days easier, more enjoyable, and more productive.

Work and caregiving

If you are shouldering both caregiving and a job, you may feel caught between conflicting responsibilities. Roughly 40% of caregivers work a full-time or part-time job. When you cannot afford to lose your job and your caregiving responsibilities encroach on your work time, the conflicts escalate. The following tips may help

you strike a better balance between these two roles.

Check work-life or employee assistance policies. Under the Family and Medical Leave Act, certain companies (including those with more than 50 employees, and public agencies) are required to offer 12 weeks of unpaid leave annually so their employees can care for a parent or spouse. Even if you can't afford to take unpaid leave, many companies find that it pays to ease the burden on valuable employees. Employers may offer flexible hours or pick up part of the cost for adult day services or home aides.

Inquire about flextime, shift changes, or telecommuting. Most flextime policies require set hours, but your supervisor may be willing to accommodate your needs by allowing you to come in late when necessary, as long as you make up the time. Taking a less desirable shift may mean you can work shorter hours or work during hours when someone else is avail-

▶ **Watch your back—literally**

Caregivers often get back injuries. Ask a professional, such as a nurse or physical therapist, to teach you the right way to shift or move the person in your care. Products like transfer boards have gliding disks, rails, or wooden balls to cut down on friction and effort. Transfer slings and belts will give you a safe, strong hold when moving someone. If the person is heavy, you may need a hoist or lift. Do not use any transfer assistive device without first getting input and training from a physical therapist. Ask your loved one's physician for a home physical therapy referral for this purpose.

able for caregiving. Telecommuting from home can be helpful, but be aware that it can be hard to get work done if the person you care for will be there and has constant needs or memory loss.

Reduce your work hours. If your employer will let you work fewer hours and you can afford to do so, part-time work or job sharing can give you more time to accomplish your caregiving responsibilities.

Set work priorities regularly. Use a day planner to map out time for uninterrupted work on projects. If you know you have an important meeting coming up, arrange for backup care so that you can get to the office, even if something goes awry at home. That may mean asking your partner, a family member, or a neighbor to cover for you, or even paying a professional to take over.

Use lunchtime and breaks judiciously. During lunchtime, it's tempting to rush around and try to complete all your errands or make up missed work, but this frenzied pace can add to your stress. Try to set aside at least part of your lunch hours each week for yourself. Spend time with co-workers, go for a walk, or read a book.

Try not to trespass on work time. Save personal calls for a short period during lunch or breaks. Do the same for personal emails and Internet research, if possible. Many companies have policies that prohibit personal use of their computers, so you may need to bring your own laptop from home, go to the library, or use your smartphone.

Personal life and caregiving

If the person you are caring for lives with you, the demands on you as the caregiver rarely let up. Running errands, making phone calls, juggling finances, and seeing the doctor can soak up many of your daily hours. It's easy to push aside anyone who is not clamoring for your attention—and even some of those who are quite vocal about wanting it. Often, your relationship with your partner, spouse, or children is squeezed unmercifully by other demands. Getting a quiet moment alone can seem like an impossible dream. In that case, the following tips can help you stay connected to the important people in your life and carve out a bit of personal time.

Bundle errands. Make a weekly master list of everything that needs to be done, including appointments, shopping, drugstore runs, and other errands. Dole out simple tasks, if possible, or do as much as you can in one trip.

Clear your schedule. Set aside time to spend with your partner or family. Start small—just one evening a week or breakfast out together if you're caring for some-

A new push for elder care programs in the workplace

The proportion of U.S. employers with elder care programs (which many corporations offer to help their employees manage caregiving tasks while still fulfilling their job responsibilities) has been steadily declining, according to the Society for Human Resource Management. But with the rise in the aging population, employers of all sizes are being advised to plan for the growing number of employees who will have elder care responsibilities in the future, according to the National Alliance for Caregiving's report *Best Practices in Workplace Eldercare*. Not only will there be an increase in the number of "old-old" (people over age 85) who will need ongoing assistance with activities of daily living, but a Gallup survey shows that more than 70% of the American workforce plans to continue working after the standard retirement age.

Employers that have introduced workplace elder care programs have experienced

- greater attraction of new employees
- greater employee retention
- improved productivity
- lower employee stress
- better employee health.

one in your home—and add to your time together when you can. Let voicemail pick up calls during certain hours, such as dinnertime. Make pre-emptive phone calls so you won't be interrupted during family or personal time. Find ways to connect with your children on a regular basis. For the younger kids, that might be a game day or nightly story time. Older kids may want to go out to a movie or dinner once a week. Brainstorm together about the activities they'd like to share.

Focus on priorities. If a clean house makes you feel good, by all means see that beds are made and housework gets done. If you prefer homemade meals to takeout or restaurants, do the cooking yourself. But look for shortcuts, too. Cook only on the weekends, and freeze meals for easier weeknight preparation. Make certain rooms

an oasis of cleanliness while being less strict about other areas of the house. Let some jobs slide, or hire help to get them done.

Setting limits

Like many worthy tasks in life, caregiving will take all you have to offer and may call for more than you can handle. Don't wait until you are ready to snap. You simply cannot do everything. Consider what you can accomplish yourself and where to set limits. You owe it to yourself and to those you love to stay healthy, reasonably happy, and sane. No one benefits when you feel you have nothing left to give.

Quell your guilt. Caregiving attracts guilt like a magnet pulls iron filings. There's always something else you could be doing or should have done. Odds are good that you already do a great deal.

Pat yourself on the back for all you give, and don't berate yourself for failing to give more.

Consider other options. Ask yourself these questions: What would happen if I were to become sick or incapacitated? Who would step in, and what would they need to do? If unpaid help couldn't handle everything, what tasks could be farmed out to professionals? What tasks would absolutely have to get done every day (washing up, dressing, eating) and which ones could be done less often or not at all?

Refuse to do it all. Acknowledge that you can't do everything yourself, and enforce that rule. The sooner you sign others on to help, the better. They'll gain more understanding of the situation and may be more likely to add duties to their job roster later.

Allow other styles. Sometimes the problem is not getting others to do a task—it's getting them to do it the way you would. While it's probably true that no one will bathe and dress your mother with all the care you lavish on her, it's also essential to let others lend a hand. Be willing to accept that perfection isn't always possible. Look the other way if the house isn't as pristine as you'd like when other people clean, or if the meals they cook aren't as tasty as yours.

Pick your battles. There are limits to what you, as a caregiver,

It's okay to say YES

When people offer to help, the answer should always be yes, according to the Family Caregiver Alliance and the National Center on Caregiving. Have a list of tasks people can help you with, whether it's bringing a meal, picking up a prescription, cleaning the home, or staying with your loved one while you run an errand. Saying yes will reinforce offers of help. It's harder to ask for help than to accept it when it's offered, so don't wait until you really need it.

can do. The person in your care may obstinately refuse to visit the doctor regularly, or to take all of his or her medications as prescribed. Talk to the doctor if you have access, and negotiate with the person when you can. Write down the elements of treatment he or she is refusing and see if you can reach some kind of mutually agreeable arrangement. Maybe you can adjust medication times to make multiple pills more palatable, or condense several doctor appointments into one or two.

Just say no. Your needs count, too. Practice saying "no" in front of the mirror or with a sympathetic friend. Try saying, "You really do need to get that done, but I'm not able to do it—who else might be able to help?" You may have to force the issue, at least the first time. People won't be able to recognize your limits if they seem infinitely expandable.

Caring for your health

As mentioned earlier, caregiving can take a marked toll on the caregiver's health. Caregivers face more depression, anxiety, and physical ailments like headaches and acid reflux than noncaregivers do. They also have nearly twice the rate of chronic conditions, such as heart disease, diabetes, and arthritis. The stresses they face on a daily basis can lead to self-harming behaviors, such as alcohol and drug abuse.

Moreover, former caregivers may not escape the health burdens after caregiving ends. One study found that 41% of people who'd cared for a spouse with Alzheimer's disease or another form of dementia had mild to severe depression up to three years after their spouse died. In general, women caregivers experience depression at a higher rate than men. Researchers have also linked caregiving to a greater risk for infections, slow wound healing, and other signs of a distressed immune system.

When caregivers are exhausted, stressed, and isolated, their health suffers. But the culprit isn't merely caregiving, which can forge a loving, healthy connection. It's the difficulty of finding the time to eat well, exercise, enjoy life, release stress, and get the rest and support you need when you're providing around-the-clock care for someone whose needs are constantly changing. The following tips can help.

Seek respite care and assistance. Take time for yourself. It can make a real difference to your state of mind. Get the assistance you need to help you take breaks.

Eat well. Plan meals and snacks ahead of time, so you won't be inclined to grab fast food or junk at hectic moments. Include plenty of vegetables and fruits in your diet, and choose whole grains over refined grain products. Limit or cut out unhealthy fats and sweets. Keep healthy snacks like air-popped popcorn or fruit on hand.

Stay active. Frequent exercise delivers proven health benefits, such as lowering cholesterol and blood pressure. It's also a potent way to beat stress. Try to get 30 to 60 minutes of moderate exercise a day, most days of the week. If you can't exercise for a full half-hour at a time, sneak in three 10-minute walks or mini-workouts throughout the day. If you can't get to the gym, start a strength training or aerobics program at home with the help of books or DVDs. When possible, include the person you're caring for, so you both stay in shape. Take a walk together, or put on some music and dance.

Stay connected. Catch up with friends by phone or email, or plan weekly walks and the occasional lunch or movie. Ask people to visit you. Also turn to online resources, such as support groups. More than half of caregivers with Internet access say online

resources have helped them deal with the stress of caregiving.

Enjoy yourself. Listen to music you like, enjoy a luxurious bath, take a yoga class, dabble in art or other creative pastimes, go out to dinner, or splurge on a massage. Regular time off helps you refresh and regroup when you start to feel burned out.

Relieving stress

When you have no outlet for stress, it compounds quickly. Has your confused father asked why he can't go back home for the 10th time in as many minutes? Have medical appointments forced you to miss work again? Are you worried about paying soaring prescription drug

A CAREGIVER'S PERSPECTIVE

"You have to know your own limits and boundaries. I need one evening off a week. At this point my mom is capable. We're hooked up by cellphones, and her dinner is prepared so she can microwave it. She's got her TV shows and her remote. I let neighbors know when she's home alone. She's also got a Lifeline. She's left alone for some periods of time, and that's what she wants."

— *Marie, 41, who moved in with her mother, who'd had a serious stroke*

bills? While you can't completely erase sources of stress in your life, you can work on solutions to problems and try other approaches to help you handle stress.

Reassess needs and brainstorm solutions. Would adult day services help once or twice a week? Would grocery shopping online give you a little more time for yourself? Can other family members step up to the plate or pitch in financially?

Release feelings. Sometimes stress stems from feelings such as anger, frustration, or dislike. Find ways to release these feelings without hurting yourself or others. Join a support group, talk with understanding friends, or consider therapy. Yell in the car with the windows rolled up. Walk up and down the hallway to burn energy.

Relax. Learn meditation and other relaxation techniques from a class, CD, book, or Web-based program. If you can't sit still long enough to meditate, try five minutes of deep breathing or guided imagery. Any time that you can spend in nature—even something as simple as watering the garden—can be particularly helpful. Certain forms of exercise—in particular, yoga, tai chi, and qigong—help increase flexibility and coordination while releasing muscle tension and enhancing inner tranquility. The time and money you'll invest will pay dividends in improved health and well-being. ♥

Resources

Organizations

Aging Life Care Association
(formerly the National Association of Professional Geriatric Care Managers)
3275 W. Ina Road, Suite 130
Tucson, AZ 85741
520-881-8008
www.aginglifecare.org
This nonprofit organization can refer you to a geriatric care manager who can help you find and oversee services for your loved one.

Caregiver Action Network
1150 Connecticut Ave. NW, Suite 501
Washington, DC 20036
202-454-3970
www.caregiveraction.org
This nonprofit association offers free publications, advocacy, and support for family caregivers.

Centers for Medicare and Medicaid Services
7500 Security Blvd.
Baltimore, MD 21244
800-633-4227 (toll-free)
www.cms.gov
This government agency provides one central location for answers to questions about Medicare and Medicaid.

Eldercare Locator
800-677-1116 (toll-free)
www.eldercare.gov
This service of the U.S. Administration on Aging connects older adults with information on financial assistance, in-home care, nursing home facilities, and other relevant services.

Family Caregiver Alliance
101 Montgomery St., Suite 2150
San Francisco, CA 94104
800-445-8106 (toll-free)
www.caregiver.org
This nonprofit organization provides education and assistance to family members and friends who are caring for a loved one.

National Academy of Elder Law Attorneys
1577 Spring Hill Road, Suite 310
Vienna, VA 22182
703-942-5711
www.naela.org
This professional association of attorneys focuses on improving the quality of legal services provided to seniors. You can search for an elder law attorney in your city on the organization's site.

National Alliance for Caregiving
4720 Montgomery Lane, Suite 205
Bethesda, MD 20814
301-718-8444
www.caregiving.org
This nonprofit coalition of organizations addresses family caregiving issues through research, policy analysis, and program development.

National Association of Area Agencies on Aging
1730 Rhode Island Ave. NW, Suite 1200
Washington, DC 20036
202-872-0888
www.n4a.org
The N4A provides information on local Area Agencies on Aging. These agencies coordinate a variety of community-based services for seniors, including legal services.

National Council on Aging
251 18th St. S, Suite 500
Arlington, VA 22202
571-527-3900
www.ncoa.org
www.benefitscheckup.org
This umbrella organization of groups and professionals is committed to enhancing seniors' lives. Individuals can use BenefitsCheckUp, an online database, to assess their eligibility for state and federal benefits programs.

National PACE Association
675 N. Washington St., Suite 300
Alexandria, VA 22314
703-535-1565
www.npaonline.org
The Program of All-Inclusive Care for the Elderly (PACE) provides a wide range of support and health care services for older adults who want to continue living independently at home.

Special Health Reports

The following Special Health Reports from Harvard Medical School provide additional information on various topics mentioned in this report. To order, call 877-649-9457 (toll-free) or go to www.health.harvard.edu.

Advance Care Planning: A guide to advance directives, living wills, and other strategies for communicating health care preferences
Muriel Gillick, M.D., Medical Editor, and Charles P. Sabatino, J.D., Legal Editor
(Harvard Medical School, 2016)

Alzheimer's Disease: A guide to diagnosis, treatment, and caregiving
Gad Marshall, M.D. Medical Editor
(Harvard Medical School, 2018)

Better Balance: Simple exercises to improve stability and prevent falls
Suzanne Salamon, M.D., and Brad Manor, Ph.D., Medical Editors
Michele Stanten, Fitness Consultant
(Harvard Medical School, 2017)

Better Bladder and Bowel Control: Practical strategies for managing incontinence
May M. Wakamatsu, M.D., Joseph A. Grocela, M.D., and Liliana Bordeianou, M.D., Medical Editors
(Harvard Medical School, 2017)